WORLD PHILOSOPH

C000089558

THE RATCHET OF SCIENCE

CURIOSITY KILLED THE CAT

For McAin

Many thanks for
all your help
with this book
all best wishes

from
Roy.

WORLD PHILOSOPHY SERIES

Additional books in this series can be found on Nova's website under the Series tab.

Additional e-books in this series can be found on Nova's website under the e-book tab.

PUBLISHED BOOKS
by Roy Calne

MEDICAL

Renal Transplantation. 1963. Edward Arnold, London (2nd edition 1967).

Lecture Notes in Surgery (with Professor Harold Ellis & Dr Chris Watson) 1965. Blackwell Scientific Publications Ltd. Oxford (13th edition 2013).

Section on Organ Transplants in 'Progress in Clinical Medicine'. 1965 Churchill, London (2nd edition 1971).

A Gift of Life. 1970. Medical and Technical Publishing Company Ltd. Aylesbury.

Clinical Organ Transplantation. 1971. Editor and contributor. Blackwell Scientific Publications Ltd. Oxford.

Immunological Aspects of Transplantation Surgery. 1973. Editor. MTP Medical and Technical Publishing Company Limited, Lancaster.

Organ Grafts ('Current Topics in Immunology' Series) 1974. Edward Arnold Ltd. London

Liver Surgery. Edited by RY Calne and G. Querci della Rovere. Riccin Editore, 1983. Padua, Italy

Liver Transplantation (Editor and contributor). Grune & Stratton, Inc. 1983. London and New York (2nd edition 1987).

A Colour Atlas of Renal Transplantation. 1984. Wolfe Medical Publications London.

Transplantation Immunology - Clinical and Experimental. Editor and contributor. Oxford University Press. 1984

A Colour Atlas of Pancreas Transplantation. 1985. Wolfe Medical Publications, London.

Living Surgical Anatomy of the Abdomen. 1987. Wolfe Medical Publications, London.

Operative Surgery. R.Y. Calne and S. Pollard. Gower Medical Publishing 1992 London and New York.

NON-MEDICAL

Too Many People. 1994. Calder Publications. London and Paris.

Art, Surgery and Transplantation. 1996. Williams & Wilkins. London

The Ultimate Gift. 1998. Hodder Headline, London.

"Scepticism – Hero & Villain" 2012. Nova Science Publishers, New York.

WORLD PHILOSOPHY SERIES

THE RATCHET OF SCIENCE

CURIOSITY KILLED THE CAT

ROY CALNE

New York

Copyright © 2014 by Nova Science Publishers, Inc.

All rights reserved. No part of this book may be reproduced, stored in a retrieval system or transmitted in any form or by any means: electronic, electrostatic, magnetic, tape, mechanical photocopying, recording or otherwise without the written permission of the Publisher.

For permission to use material from this book please contact us:
Telephone 631-231-7269; Fax 631-231-8175
Web Site: http://www.novapublishers.com

NOTICE TO THE READER

The Publisher has taken reasonable care in the preparation of this book, but makes no expressed or implied warranty of any kind and assumes no responsibility for any errors or omissions. No liability is assumed for incidental or consequential damages in connection with or arising out of information contained in this book. The Publisher shall not be liable for any special, consequential, or exemplary damages resulting, in whole or in part, from the readers' use of, or reliance upon, this material. Any parts of this book based on government reports are so indicated and copyright is claimed for those parts to the extent applicable to compilations of such works.

Independent verification should be sought for any data, advice or recommendations contained in this book. In addition, no responsibility is assumed by the publisher for any injury and/or damage to persons or property arising from any methods, products, instructions, ideas or otherwise contained in this publication.

This publication is designed to provide accurate and authoritative information with regard to the subject matter covered herein. It is sold with the clear understanding that the Publisher is not engaged in rendering legal or any other professional services. If legal or any other expert assistance is required, the services of a competent person should be sought. FROM A DECLARATION OF PARTICIPANTS JOINTLY ADOPTED BY A COMMITTEE OF THE AMERICAN BAR ASSOCIATION AND A COMMITTEE OF PUBLISHERS.

Additional color graphics may be available in the e-book version of this book.

Library of Congress Cataloging-in-Publication Data

Calne, Roy Yorke, author.
 The ratchet of science : curiosity killed the cat / Roy Calne (Dept. of Medicine and Surgery, National University of Singapore).
  pages cm. -- (Science, evolution and creationism)
  Includes bibliographical references and index.
  ISBN: 978-1-63117-861-0 (softcover)
  1. Science--Moral and ethical aspects. 2. Science--Forecasting. I. Title.
  Q175.35.C35 2014
  174'.95--dc23
        2014014973

Published by Nova Science Publishers, Inc. † *New York*

I would like to dedicate the book to Patsy, my wife, Donald Calne and Prof KO Lee.

CONTENTS

Contents

ACKNOWLEDGMENTS

I wish to thank especially Allen Packwood for access to papers in the Archives in Churchill College and for his personal encouragement.

I am also extremely grateful to Allan McDonald, Martin Thomson, William Wall, K. O. Lee and my brother, Donald Calne, for their careful reading of the text and their extremely helpful suggestions. I thank Jenny Richards and Jennifer Cummings for typing and correcting progressive versions.

FOREWORD

Gustav Born

In this book Roy Calne provides a comprehensive yet concise and deeply thoughtful overview of the contributions of science to human progress, and of the resulting benefits and dangers. This brief preface cannot do more than pay admiring tribute to Calne's achievement with this important book, which follows on his invaluable professional work in a new and particularly difficult branch of surgery.

'Ratchet' in the title means 'impelled to go forward', which is an intrinsic characteristic of science. Natural science germinated only twice in human history: first in ancient Greece where it did not survive; and for the second time in post-Reformation Europe, where it did although, as the persecution of Galileo shows, even then it was touch and go. The 'one-way street' of scientific history is set out in these pages in all its complexities; from early historical records to the ever-accelerating process now, with apt comments on the beneficial and the dangerous consequences of science.

Roy Calne begins with a quotation from the physicist Lise Meitner: "Science makes people reach selflessly for truth and objectivity". Yes indeed: that is how it should be, and almost always is. Happily, exceptions are very rare and never seriously impede the progress of science. Instead, they sometimes give rise to ludicrous events. Many years ago my niece Sylvia, working as a laboratory technician in New York, phoned me in London: "Uncle uncle, have you already heard of our painted mice?" A young researcher named Summerlin had falsely claimed success with grafting skin from black onto white mice which were not immunologically compatible: he had of course painted the "grafts" on the skin with black ink. The great immunologist Peter Medawar played an only half amused role in showing up this fraud.

Unfortunately, there is nothing funny about research for war. Science-based weaponry, as everyone knows or should know, has become a danger to human survival. In the First World War, poison gas was introduced as a weapon by Germany under the direction of the chemist (and Nobel Laureate) Fritz Haber. When the Nazis took over the German government in 1933 Harber, a Jew, fled to Cambridge where, because of his poison gas history, he was ostracised by the great physicist Lord Rutherford. In contrast, a young researcher named Parker, who many years ago worked for the Medical Research Council, refused a large increase in salary offered for joining the Chemical Weapons Establishment at Porton Down, saying he would never do that kind of work. My father, the physicist Max Born foresaw the dangerous misuse of science for war many years ago. Expelled by the German Nazis, like many Jewish scientists, Max would have nothing to do with what he called "the atomic devilry" underway in Los Alamos.

This devilry became evident to all the World in 1945, when the great Japanese cities of Hiroshima and Nagasaki were destroyed by the first atomic bombs. These bombs had been developed as a consequence of the discovery in 1939 of nuclear fission by the physicist Lise Meitner who, as Roy Calne stresses, was appalled by the mass-murdering application of her immense discovery. The atomic bombs caused the surrender of Japan in August 1945. Some three months afterwards, as a young medical officer in the British Army, I was one of three foreigners who first beheld the devastation that was Hiroshima; a memory that it is impossible to obliterate even over a long lifespan. I still have the distressed correspondence with my father Max beginning on that 6th August 1945, about the horror of this new weapon and its implications for the future. Incidentally, Hiroshima initiated some of my later research. Apart from some 80,000 people killed outright by the bomb, over many months afterwards thousands were still dying from uncontrollable haemorhage: the radiation had destroyed the production in the bone marrow of thrombocytes, also called platelets, circulating cells specialised to clump together in injured vessels to stop bleeding. Our research elucidated the mechanism of this reaction.

Overall, there seems so far to have been little limitation on the utilisation of scientific advances for unethical purposes, except fortunately in human genetics. One of the things about such advances which produce practical technologies that should perhaps be disturbing is how they are made use of by most people without apparently understanding or indeed even marvelling at what they can do: no one ever before could not only talk with but also see halfway around the World, as we can, from London to our daughter in California. In medicine the latest advances in science are transformed into diagnostic devices and effective treatments in what feels to this old doctor like the blink of an eye. Nowadays, limits of treatments are imposed more often by financial rather than by technical considerations.

Happily, medical work still remains subject to ethical limitations. However, a comparatively recent branch of medical science is genomics. According to Anna Middleton and her colleagues in Cambridge, the technical progress for determining genotypes appears to be outstripping the newly devised ethics.

With hyperdestructive scientific capabilities in the hands of dictators as well as of democracies, human survival will depend on who wins the race between irrational antagonisms and the rationality required for coexistence. As Roy Calne rightly says, permeation of all aspects of human life by science is now so powerful that our dominant issue is the question, how much control should there be of genuine ethical scientific investigations, and at what stage does this control become counterproductive? So the book ends with a plea for clarity about our present concerns. It advances that clarity greatly and should be read and remembered.

22nd February 2014

INTRODUCTION

The March of Science is a perilous journey.
Science cannot be unlearned

"Science makes people reach selflessly for truth and objectivity; it teaches people to accept reality, with wonder and admiration, not to mention the deep awe and joy that the natural order of things brings to the true scientist".

Figure 1. Painting of Lise Meitner as a young scientist (RYC).

A poetic quote from Lise Meitner, who as a young physicist discovered and named nuclear fission, explains the common, almost romantic quest for knowledge and its beauty for humans that can result from success in scientific endeavours. Paul Bowersox Nuclear Café Blog commenting on Lise Meitner's ode to Science, continued "and since today is Valentine's Day to this author, this reads like a love letter to the Universe. Lovely, indeed".

Lise Meitner was appalled by the harnessing of nuclear fission to produce a weapon for mass murder and stated on a number of occasion that she would have nothing to do with a bomb and she refused to be recruited to the Los Alamos atomic bomb project. But indirectly she was the midwife to the birth of thermonuclear weapons. Human curiosity has revealed knowledge of nature that once discovered cannot be unlearned, hence the title "The Ratchet of Science". The inescapable truth is that once something new is learned or invented it cannot be put back, the genie is out of the bottle and has escaped for all time. The theme of this book is an attempt to explain the benefits and dangers that are the consequences of science.

Thanks to the kind help of Allen Packwood, Archivist at Churchill College, Cambridge, I have been able to study some of the correspondence between scientists involved in the Manhattan Project expressing their concern after the use of thermonuclear weapons and the postwar nuclear arms race.

I will consider curiosity historically from the earliest examples revealed in archaeology, ancient history and medieval writings and survey the huge acceleration in the military applications of discoveries, dating from the invention of gunpowder by the Chinese to produce fireworks to the internal combustion engine, electricity and its many applications, flight, nuclear fission and the internet. Tim Berners-Lee, who invented the worldwide web with the intention of its use for the benefit of mankind and deliberately did not file a patent so that it would be a pure gift to humanity, recently voiced his concern at the international hacking revelations of

Edward Snowden, a story for Berners-Lee that is a parallel to that of Lise Meitner. He has recently advocated a "Magna Carta" style protection of users of the World Wide Web from intrusive government surveillance as an infringement of their human rights.

I do not pretend to be a specialist of human nature but my medical background, especially in the difficult early history of organ transplantation, leads me to doubt that there has been a serious change for the good in human nature. Recent barbarities in Syria and even in the streets of London and Boston, demonstrate the extreme rapidity with which civilisation can descend to butchery of fellow human beings. Nevertheless with current access to weaponry, although much devilment can be caused by a few people or even a lone terrorist, it is unlikely that nations could be threatened by such a terrorist plot. These strictures do not apply to nations possessing nuclear weapons with delivery capability and storage facilities, where an unbalanced dictator could let loose a thermonuclear war or even with machismo rhetoric cause pre-emptive retaliatory release of atomic weapons by a fearful threatened enemy. In the background is the very real possibility of human error no matter how many elaborate safeguards are in place.

Curiosity is a hard-wired feature of the human psyche recorded in the Bible and Greek mythology. Many political and religious regimes have deliberately repressed this tendency to enquire but inevitably individuals have escaped from such tyranny and investigated nature. The observations made constitute science and this knowledge has completely transformed the way we live. I have listed some of these developments with an attempt to explain how they have impinged on our lives. Advances in science have occurred by deliberately targeted study and with chance findings of great importance confronting what Pasteur referred to as "the prepared mind", usually discovered by an individual already trained in the scientific method.

The quality of life that we enjoy is largely the result of scientific advances and I have explained in more detail how some medical advances occurred, and especially organ transplantation – my own special interest - now an established effective form of treatment for many people who before would have been doomed to an early death. I have also outlined approaches to new medical science in the field of stem cells and gene therapy, which are at an early stage but almost certainly will provide valuable therapy in years to come.

There is a continuing debate concerning the distribution of funds between "Blue Sky" pure science, science pursued for direct application and technological development. The choice of "Blue Sky" science is motivated by curiosity but often with a subliminal thought of possible applications. On the other hand, the current fashion for favouring translational science maybe mistaken as many important applications have derived from "Blue Sky" approaches. To be forced to choose a translational subject with restrictions maybe distasteful to some of the most talented scientists with gifts in lateral thinking. Modification, development and improvement occur with all worthwhile scientific advances and certainly behave in a ratchet-like manner.

It is common experience for a new hypothesis to be greeted with scepticism by the establishment and the chapter in this book on medicine has material published in a review of scepticism by Nova Scientific Publications. The dual role of hero and villain is important since scepticism can be helpful in discouraging exaggerated and spurious claims, but can be harmful in inhibiting the blossoming of new ideas coming from enthusiastic young scientists who may be permanently discouraged before they get a chance to prove or disprove their hypotheses. The unexpected and sometimes horrific applications of science initially aimed at improving the lot of mankind can be hijacked to destructive potential completely alien and contrary to the objectives of the scientist who did the original work, exemplified in the story of Lise Meitner.

A new approach to war has evolved with unmanned drones, currently targeting individuals directly from a computer in a different continent. Added to this are the capabilities of interfering with controls of weapons and the electricity supply of military installations and national use of electricity, which is an essential feature of modern society.

All this could be construed as the ravings of a prophet of doom, so what positive thoughts can one hope for changes to safeguard humanity. Since the Second World War the enormity of the destructive potential of nuclear weapons has been an important threat in preventing their use, albeit with some close-run incidents. Perhaps it is not unreasonable to look at modern science with its potential for harm to have a responsibility to society to conjure up a solution. There are many scientists in the world deeply concerned with the dangers outlined above but to get them to work together would certainly be expensive and difficult. Shortly after the carnage of the Second World War scientists, politicians and religious leaders were appalled by the threat of nuclear war and many were active in lobbying for global control and eventual destruction of all atomic weapons. Although their objectives have not been realised their activities may not have been in vain, since no further use has been made in war of nuclear weapons in the past 65 years. This surely must justify some hope for the future of human civilisation.

The collaborative concentrations of experts in mathematics and physics from many nations working in Switzerland at CERN could be a focus for an institute devoted to the idea of trying to make people live and let live safely. Scientists from appropriate specialities together with politicians, philosophers and religious leaders could be visitors to such an institute to interact and contribute to the objective of world peace.

In the context of long-term cosmic history one day all such effort will be unnecessary but even in the short-term natural disaster could determine our fate as occurred in the global elimination of the dinosaurs with a massive meteor or comet strike or unprecedented volcanic and tectonic plate activity. No doubt some species would survive but there is no guarantee that *Homo sapiens* would be amongst them.

Curiosity is part of human nature and so is killing, both beautifully recorded in the book of Genesis (Figure 2). The danger of knowledge is only too clear. "Science" means knowledge, but in the modern context it is knowledge confirmed by reproducibility of observations and more specifically by experiments.

I will examine some advances in knowledge which have changed human behaviour. None of these would have been possible without the unique gifts of abstract thought and language, the distinguishing features of *Homo sapiens*. All living creatures, animals and plants need food, water, a suitable environment and the ability to reproduce, otherwise the species will perish. In modern times man has been successful in greatly reducing infant mortality and prolonging adult life so that the advocacy of most major religions to "go forth and multiply" has led to an increase in the human population severely threatening availability of the necessities of life for humans and countless species of animals and plants.

Figure 2. The Good and the Bad sequelae of partaking of the forbidden fruit (RYC from the book "Too Many People."

There is an important distinction between scientific observations that can be reproduced without difficulty, compared to science which is in doubt, where the data may be conflicting and the conclusions unconvincing.

Traditionally science should be open and available to all in published form, but secrecy and censorship are sometimes enforced, especially in times of conflict or anticipation and preparation for war, for example the development of the atomic bomb and the decoding of the German encrypted codes.

Although "fairness" is a mantra of contemporary politicians in democracies "fairness" is a nonsense. The distribution of genetic material is certainly not equal nor fair, nor are most political and economic benefits or restrictions bestowed upon the individual by the state. Another much lauded democratic attribute is "free speech" but this is restricted in every society, although the penalties have a wide spectrum stretching from burning at the stake to general disapproval. Try making a joke at US immigration!

Uncertainty is part of human knowledge and the greater the uncertainty the more intense will be the argument and the more powerful the faith exhibited by vociferous contenders. If an observation can be repeated often and successfully, for example the nature of the solar system regarding the movements of the planets, there is no place for serious disagreement, but with the variety of scientific observations relevant to climate change, different scientific fields are involved together with important and powerful political and economic considerations explaining the continuous and often acrimonious debate.

Competition is inevitable, well-recognised in Darwin's arguments in the struggle for survival. The complexity of human nature is evident to all. Every individual will have reserves of compassion but also of hatred. A perusal of history reveals that in most societies power has been sought and achieved by a variety of strategies, often involving violence. Sadly a popular, unbalanced psychopathic personality does not exclude an individual from being

peacefully elected in a democratic process and then achieving the
pinnacle of power to enforce an irrational and often vicious even
murderous dictatorial regime as occurred with Hitler's rise to power
in Germany in the 1930s. Democracy has been cynically compared
to jumping on a bus and then when no longer going in the direction
planned by the leader, the democracy omnibus is abandoned and
changed to a police state of doctrinal or religious tyranny.

Each advance in repeatable science remains as a record for
humanity that cannot be erased. The corpus of science is retained by
a ratchet that does not allow removal; there is no "delete" button.
The science discussed in this volume may or may not have been
pursued primarily with a view to an improvement in the lethality of
weapons, but at each stage with new discoveries and developments,
the possibility of military use has been considered. With early
weapons the amount of destructive potential was limited, but
recently in a rapidly accelerating manner, new weapons have
changed the scale and nature of killing power in a terrifying manner.

The subjects to be considered start with stone implements, slings,
bows and arrows and then a major change in the Bronze Age with
the ability to work copper and tin to produce useful aids for living
but also more effective weapons. Ships were designed using both
human effort for propulsion and the power of the wind. The Iron
Age was a leap further in the construction of new weapons each
providing important superiority over enemies if they had not
developed similar armouries. The element of surprise could outwit
the enemy.

The medieval Chinese invented printing and gunpowder for
fireworks. Both of these were utilised effectively and aggressively
by Western nations. Printing enabled information and religious
beliefs to be spread widely and rapidly but the early printers were in
danger of torture and execution if they printed heretical or seditious
material. There were rapid advances with the development of
engines, changing the pattern of manufacture with the "Spinning
Jenny" and travel and communication with steam engines to power

the railways and maritime voyages. The internal combustion engine enabled further advances in travel but also the production of tanks and engines for powered flight for aircraft designed for aggression. The steam turbine and jet engines took these advances to another stage of speed and potential destructive power.

In the past 100 years there has been a massive increase in the production of new killing agents including poison gas, germs, atomic energy and the now perhaps the most dangerous of all, cyber aggression. The discovery and utilisation of electricity conferred enormous benefits but also spawned applications that have far reaching consequences, some of which have advanced civilisation, but others have aggressive potential. Until the telegraph was invented information could take weeks or months to reach the intended recipient. The far outposts of empires, relied on horseback, ships and even visual signals and carrier pigeons for issuing instructions, which were often useless by the time the orders arrived. A new leader might have supplanted the old, an important battle could have been won or lost and the season may have changed to have a crucial effect on the conduct of war. The Roman and British empires both suffered from the time delays in the despatch of orders from the capital, so generals in the periphery of the empire were forced to make their own decisions and often used the opportunity to develop their own agendas in mounting rebellions. This particular dangerous freedom as perceived by the ruler was changed very quickly with the electronic telegraphic communication. The flow of information proliferated with ever-increasing efficiency with the introduction of telephone, radio, television, the internet, social networks and the ever more menacing surveillance from orbiting satellites and secret intelligence gatherers. The possibility of aggressively interfering with security and weapons-control is a grave risk. Such techniques have already been pioneered and will certainly become increasingly effective. Each advance although requiring complex safeguards opens up the likelihood of human error and accidental unleashing of destruction. Would it be possible to prevent dictators, often megalomaniac psychopaths, lacking compassion and humanity but with absolute authority, from using new killing tools?

History fails to give an optimistic prognosis but so far sanity has prevented nuclear war that could destroy *Homo sapiens*. Robert Oppenheimer's much quoted observation from the Hindu scripture - Bhagavad Gita *"Now I have become death the destroyer of worlds"*, on witnessing the test of the first atomic chain reaction expressed his horror of the devastation available to his 'brain child'. This resonates with much of what we know of human nature. It requires great optimism to be convinced that the compassion of humanity to "live and let live" will prevail.

Chapter I

PUGWASH AND BOMBMAKING

Albert Einstein commenting on the possibility of constructing an atomic bomb accurately predicted, *"Once the Military have this, they will use it no matter what you say"*.

Just after the Atom Bomb attacks on Hiroshima and Nagasaki:
August 1945 –A letter from Max Born, Nobel Prize winning nuclear physicist, to his son Gustav:

> "How can anybody foretell the effects of any new discovery? How could you keep people from pondering about magnifying some minute effect? All that seems like an avalanche. If man is so constructed that his curiosity leads him to self-destruction there is no hope for him. But I am not convinced that he is so constructed, for beside his brain he has his heart".

Max Born's letter to his son, Gustav, eloquently describes the alarm and extreme worry that the damage and destruction of the atomic bombs caused reasonable people throughout the world. Born's hope that man beside his brain has a heart must be true for the overwhelming majority, but what about the relatively few convinced terrorists consumed with hatred and obsessions often fuelled by distorted religious interpretation. How much harm could they inflict?

Following the dropping of two thermonuclear weapons, one on Hiroshima and the other on Nagasaki the whole world was shocked and Japan was horrified to witness at close quarters the wicked destruction of people near the epicentre, where humans were literally vapourised, the whole living body instantaneously projected as a shadow imprinted on the wall (Figure 3). A little further from the epicentre the flesh was ripped out of people and left as hanging shards for the poor doctors, who could do nothing for the victims.

Figure 3a. The terrible menace of the mushroom of a thermo-nuclear explosion, image of the British test explosion on Christmas Island.

Figure 3b. Image of a man vapourised as a shadow on the wall by the Hiroshima bomb.

Since the beginning of time war has been a terrible thing, causing dreadful suffering to those engaged in the war and often involving completely innocent bystanders. No doubt the thermonuclear weapons in Japan hastened the end of the war and indirectly saved many lives, but the question remains why are humans, who by definition are capable of reasoning, prepared to engage in such mutually destructive events? In Western countries and Soviet Russia many prominent citizens, including scientists, politicians, philosophers and religious leaders voiced their anguish and concern but there was no obvious solution as to how to prevent similar occurrences in the future. A group of specially motivated and worried individuals planned to meet in a relatively small conference to discuss the situation and try to propose possible remedies. Needless to say this was not easy as there was at the time a major cultural chasm between communism and capitalism with the gulf enlarging continuously, with each side viewing the other with grave suspicion and a reluctance even to have discourse to attempt to find common ground. Nevertheless, a meeting, hosted by a wealthy industrialist, Cyrus Eaton, was convened in the small Nova Scotia town of Pugwash and this was the forerunner of a number of similar conferences. It was interesting and sad that many individual agendas were disturbed and feathers ruffled just in the process of organising the meeting.

The first Pugwash conference was held in 1957. It followed a manifesto issued in 1955 by Bertrand Russell and Albert Einstein (Figure 4) 22 scientists participated from the United States, Soviet Union, Japan, United Kingdom, Canada, Australia, Austria, China, France and Poland; so a wide range of concerned scientists.

I had access to important archival papers of that time, and essential to the organising of the Pugwash meetings were the conscientious and persistent efforts of Joseph Rotblat, a nuclear scientist and later winner of the Nobel Peace Prize, who together with Leo Szilard, resigned from the Manhattan project on conscientious grounds. His papers and those of fellow nuclear physicist, Max Born, revealed the strivings for a meeting of serious, respected men of peace, in the hope of producing an influential manifesto for future generations, to prevent war. There are interesting letters between Joseph Rotblat, Bertrand Russell, Albert Einstein and Max Born, which clearly show the difficulties involved in trying to get any useful action for peace. There were also movements in many countries to promote peace and strong lobbies organised to try and secure the destruction of all nuclear weapons. Sadly this has not been possible. Nations that have acquired nuclear weapons regard them not only as instruments for defence and potential attack, but also seem to have a feeling that the atomic weapons are "trophies" indicating how clever and powerful the individual nations are.

Figure 4. Notice to the world – a manifesto from Albert Einstein and Bertram Russell, warning of the dangers and consequences of a thermo-nuclear war.

I have worked and taught in Cambridge University for 45 years and inevitably have had contact with many people, highly regarded in academia as being possessed of exceptional intelligence but despite trying to seek a connection I have been quite unable to determine any correlation between the degree of intelligence and understanding or use of common sense. Neither am I convinced that there is a negative correlation but in the exchanges between Bertrand Russell and Albert Einstein one would have thought together they would form a constellation of the greatest wisdom possible, yet they both agreed that a powerful world government, with its own international global army, navy and air force would be necessary and essential to maintain peace. This seems to me to be an extremely naive wish that anything practical could come from such a concept. In the British Isles one government has been consistently unable to govern. Secession from central government seems to be a general wish of Ireland, Scotland, Wales and even regions of England. If people speaking the same language and having roughly the same ethical outlook cannot agree on a central government, what chance is there for the rest of the world? A direct sequel of these observations is the total impossibility of the idea of a global armed force that would be effective and acceptable to individual nations. Despite these negative thoughts, Pugwash and similar conferences and campaigns to "ban the bomb" would seem to have had an effect in concentrating the minds of powerful politicians so that the "MAD" principle of mutual assured destruction if any nation used thermonuclear weapons is constantly influencing policy. These factors have been important in maintaining peace but the macho rhetoric of national leaders has, together with military and economic circumstances led to very serious confrontation that frightened the world. In 1962 Soviet missiles were dispatched to Cuba with a potential to be armed with thermonuclear weapons. Only at the last moment did Nikita Khrushcev blink and the freighters carrying the missiles turned around back to Russia (Figure 5). There are naturally extremely carefully installed fail-safe arrangements in place to prevent accidental release of thermonuclear weapons and to ensure that responsibility for decision making is controlled and curtailed. Unfortunately wherever there are humans involved there will be mistakes. In 1980 a thermonuclear device came close to a catastrophic detonation in Damascus, Arkansas. There have been serious accidents in atomic power stations, the worst in Chernobyl in the Ukraine in 1986, but also in the US, the UK and recently in Fukushima in Japan. Perhaps the biggest danger of initiation of a thermonuclear war would be the result of human error, or retaliation for the incorrect perception by a nation that the potential enemy had directed an attack against them. The rapid crescendo of launching thermonuclear devices from land, sea and air does not bear thinking about, since civilisation as we know it would be seriously in jeopardy.

Figure 5. US Neptune aircraft shadowing the Soviet ship carrying missiles (1962).

The Cold War continued into the 1980s when there was fear throughout the world that a thermonuclear conflict was inevitable. Ronald Reagan labelled the Soviet Union an "Evil Empire" and deployed cruise missiles to Europe.

A civil servant drafted a farewell message for the Queen to broadcast to the people saying:

> "We all know that the dangers facing us today are greater by far than at any time in our long history. The enemy is not the soldier with his rifle nor even the airman prowling the skies above our cities and towns but the deadly power of abused technology. But whatever terrors lie in wait for us all the

qualities that have helped to keep our freedom intact twice already during this sad century will once more be our strength".

International conventions to avoid certain weapons perceived to be particularly vile, for example chemical weapons especially poison gas and germ warfare have probably been a restraining influence in their use in wars that have occurred since WWII. However recently there have been flagrant abuses, especially in the use of Sarin gas in Syria. The consequences were relayed globally on television and demonstrated the dreadful destruction of humans, particularly poignant the sight of suffering women and children. An attempt is being made to destroy these weapons but vicious civil war continues with conventional arms that also cause death and dreadful wounds.

A rational scenario for safety is not easily forthcoming to those seeking peace and for humans to "live and let live" which would be the common wish of the vast majority of mankind. Sadly we are driven to the back foot clinging desperately to the one remaining symbol of sanity and goodwill, namely HOPE.

BOMBMAKING

"I know not with what weapons World War III will be fought, but World War IV will be fought with sticks and stones."

Albert Einstein

To construct a thermonuclear weapon is not a task for a crazy terrorist in a garage, at least not at present. To release the energy of an atomic bomb the heavy radioactive elements uranium or plutonium are required that will then be subjected to a bombardment by neutrons to cause explosive fission of the material. A critical mass of the target is required and also controlled delivery of neutrons. Two uranium isotopes are involved U238 and U235 but only the U235 is a suitable fission product and this exists at 1% in uranium that is mined in rocks. Enrichment and purification of uranium is a complicated process to bring the percentage of 235 up to around 90%. This involves multiple expensive and precision-made gas centrifuges which have featured prominently in the international news regarding Iran's nuclear ambitions. Plutonium also requires a complicated process involving heavy hydrogen in order to secure fissionable material. To obtain the essential materials in sufficient quantities and purity therefore involves major resources that are currently only available to nation states. The assembly of the bomb is also complicated with many design variations to decrease size and increase effects. A primary minor conventional explosion sets off a chain reaction which rapidly leads to the extraordinary release of energy with its well-known destructive capabilities. The assembled weapon currently weighs around 50 kilograms although smaller packages have been produced weighing as little as 20 kilos.

The next stage in the gruesome process of unleashing a thermonuclear war is how to deliver the lethal package. At the end of World War Two in 1945 the two bombs were dropped from conventional aeroplanes, Boeing B29 bombers. Many different missiles have been developed for arming with atom bombs. The thermonuclear warhead can be fitted to an intercontinental missile which is launched into space and directed at a target. The missile can be fired from land silos, warships and especially submarines which can deliver the Polaris missiles from beneath the sea. The warhead could also be fired from a drone aircraft or a robotic landcraft.

Much of the development of thermonuclear weapons is secret and therefore not available for public scrutiny but reports released from time to time, suggest that there has been great expenditure and efforts by all nations possessing atomic weapons to modify them to have greater killing and destructive power and to be in smaller packages that can be more easily delivered. These secret refinements of the bomb do not provide any reassurance that they will never be used.

With current technologies it is clear that a major strike with thermonuclear weapons would require the resources of a sizeable nation state, which itself would inevitably be a target for immediate or even pre-emptive retaliation. This whole scenario is an Armageddon that all sane people and reasonable nations would strive to prevent, since the consequences would be dire, not only for the initial combatants but also for the rest of the world which would be subject to lethal and long lasting collateral damage.

Chapter II

HISTORICAL BACKGROUND

It is likely that the early hunter gatherers, *Homo sapiens* would have developed a tribal knowledge from trial and error or trial and succeed, in their ability at hunting and gathering and improving their general comfort. They used stones as missiles and then the shaping of stones to make knives and arrow heads for use in their hunting. A major advance was to make fire for cooking food and keeping warm. Tribal co-operation and loyalty gives solidarity and group identity. The whole tribe would move to a new location when resources of the old one were exhausted. The move might involve encountering another tribe and although peaceful co-existence could be an option, the techniques and equipment used for hunting would be valuable if conflict ensued.

We do not know if language and abstract thought occurred simultaneously. It appears that some primitive tribes have no concept or interest in abstract ideas and the Piraha, a tribe of the Amazon, has no words to indicate what happened yesterday and plans for tomorrow, nevertheless they hunt and gather quite successfully. They have no words for numbers or colours and no religion and are not easily persuaded to understand or adopt missionary efforts at explaining religion.

The increasingly complicated changes in human culture have some similarity to the biology of the evolution of the eye. The ability to distinguish between light and shade, day and night has been regarded as an evolutionary advantage but to improve on this simple sense to permit accurate image analysis and rapid understanding to recognise the danger of predators and also the possibility of obtaining food is clearly a significant advance in the fitness to cope with the environment. It has been established that the eye evolved independently in different species many times, with the definitive models having specifications unique for the species in question, for example, the wave length of light that can be perceived, the field of vision and also the accuracy of the vision in the extraordinary visual resolution available to birds of prey. In an analogous manner humans developed new concepts and inventions in different locations often at about the same time. Fire was probably observed as a result of accident but to harness it so that it could be started, stopped and controlled conferred great benefits in cooking food and keeping warm.

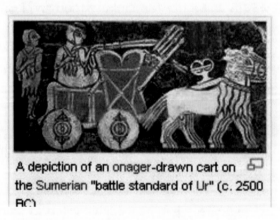

A depiction of an onager-drawn cart on 🔗
the Sumerian "battle standard of Ur" (c. 2500
BC)

Figure 6. Sumerian battle standard of Ur circa. 2500 BC. Early image of wheels adapted for war.

Slings, bows and arrows were invented independently in different parts of the world by primitive tribes. The construction of boats for fishing and to seek better habitats with the ability to travel across water, improved the quality of life and also gave advantages in aggressive exploits against competitors.

A heavy object immoveable on its own could be transported by rolling on a log, using the circular circumference of a natural tree trunk. This principle was susceptible to advantageous modification by using a transverse section of the trunk with a central hole for an axle, constituting the wheel. It seems that wheels were invented in different parts of the world and used to construct carts and also chariots of war, documented in art by the Sumerians (Figure 6).

The four great inventions of the Chinese of gunpowder, paper, printing and the compass were all developed and often improved upon by other civilisations, particularly in the middle east and Western Europe by both Islam and Byzantium. Ingenious modifications could greatly enhance the effectiveness of an invention and confer a major advantage to the nation that first used it in war before the secret was discovered by opponents. In mediaeval times the English longbow could be loaded quicker and aimed more accurately than the crossbow and was a major factor in victory in the battle of Crecy (Figure 7). There are many examples in modern times of a similar nature, some of which will be discussed later.

Figure 7. The battle of Crecy – British longbow men had a superior weapon in speed and accuracy.

Within a corpus of knowledge scientific advances tend to occur contemporaneously in different civilisations and if the first revelation of a scientific breakthrough had not occurred in a certain place it would nevertheless have occurred somewhere else sooner or later. The unraveling of the DNA structure and an understanding of how this conferred the ability for cells to reproduce and synthesise proteins would probably have been worked out quite soon after the classical paper that Crick and Watson wrote in Nature 1953 if they had not already solved it. In contrast in the Arts there would be no justification for a similar argument of inevitability. If Beethoven had not been born there would never have been a 9th Symphony and the wonderful paintings of Renaissance artists with their individual signatures of style could only evolve from the hands of those individuals. However even this argument has some weakness, since there were constellations of almost miraculous talent at a certain time and place. Michelangelo, Leonardo de Vinci and Raphael were contemporaries and knew each other albeit without much evidence of friendliness. There must have been a corpus of skills and knowledge that constituted a "centre of progress and excellence" amongst these great artists. The same could be said for the influence of Haydn and Mozart on Beethoven. There is much room for debate in these matters but it is not unreasonable to view the achievements in the arts in a similar manner to those in science. They are joyful gifts from humans to humans that hopefully cannot be lost and can be regarded as the consequence of a beneficial ratchet-like effect.

To return to early history, the unanswerable questions of "why are we here ,where do we come from and where will we go?" could provide tribal leaders with convincing fictional explanations expressed in folklore and myth which often involved, singing, chanting, drum beating, dancing and ritual sacrifice both of animals and humans. This was the likely origin of the power and persuasiveness of early and later religious leaders and is still practiced in its primitive mode by the shamans and witchdoctors of Africa. Magic relics improvised from coconut shells, skulls and hollowed-out wood and stone became part of the rituals. An important development was the discovery that after moulding, clay could be transformed by heat into vessels for storage of provisions of water, oil and wine. The fashioning of ritualistic sculptures and painting occurred at least 30,000 years ago. We know that our forebears had remarkable skills in visual arts. In caves some of the wall paintings can only be seen after a long and uncomfortable crawl through narrow tunnels. Many paintings featured animals being hunted or animals which turned the tables so that the hunters became hunted. Cave paintings are beautiful and they probably had important religious significance.

Image-making was used to communicate information on danger, where to find food and water and, in China, developed into the ideograms of a written language. A huge advance from the Stone Age was the discovery that tin and copper could be heated to produce bronze, which was cast and hammered to make useful tools, instruments and ornaments and efficient knives, spear heads, daggers and swords.

Bronze was a very important material that accelerated advances in civilisation. The successor to the use of bronze was the discovery of iron, which had certain advantages although it was difficult to work with and required higher temperatures to melt than bronze. When carbon was added to iron, a very hard and resistant new material that retains the sharpness of a cutting edge resulted in the Iron Age succeeding the Bronze Age. The progression from the use of stone to bronze and then iron enhanced the comfort of living and also the efficacy of weapons. Cultivation of crops required settlements in villages and the necessity for co-operation in working together and usually involved an hierarchy under a ruler. The early Pharaohs 4000 years ago acquired in one man the triple role of god, lawmaker and law enforcer. Adopting all these three roles was for centuries remarkably successful and involved major exploitation of slaves for hard labour and also some with special skills. But gradually as civilisation developed the all-powerful Pharaohs devolved some of the influence and responsibilities on vassals, who needed to be watched carefully for signs of rebellion and usurping for themselves the roles of the Pharaoh. Following the "Arab Spring" Mohamed Morsi declared himself to be Pharaoh but his CV was not up to the mark. North Korea is the sole exception in modern times that maintains this tyranny of god, lawmaker and law enforcer in one individual.

There was a succession of extremely powerful and effective empires around the Mediterranean, in Persia and China, each maintaining a large army with horses trained for war and, with the invention of the wheel, the horses were harnessed to chariots. Religious differences were often the excuse for war and conquest. The conflict between Christian nations and Islam began soon after the emergence of Islam as a significant force. In Constantinople in 700 AD the Christians gained a temporary advantage with a victory at sea using a new secret weapon of flaming "Greek oil" projected from their ships (Figure 8). Adaptations of new inventions to make weapons more lethal have continued ever since.

Figure 8. Greek Fire Flaming Oil – a secret weapon giving them advantage over the Saracens in the Siege of Constantinople in the 7th Century.

The invention of the magnetic compass gave a reasonable idea of where mariners were at any one time and the direction in which they were travelling. The British Empire was extremely successful for many years on the basis of trade, navigation, business acumen and power, enforced by the might of the British East India Company. With its own large army and navy it became *de facto* an arm of the State to impose a colonised Empire often at the expense of exploitation of the subjected nations. On a smaller scale the Dutch East India Company did likewise. Although warships propelled by enslaved oarsmen were used in combat for many centuries, transport, navigation and conquest relied mainly on the power of the wind and its unpredictability was the cause of many maritime disasters.

THE RENAISSANCE 16ᵀᴴ – 17ᵀᴴ CENTURIES

The Renaissance was the pivotal point that led to the questioning of received wisdom, dictated by the Church hierarchy. In Western Europe natural philosophy started to have green shoots with discussions in the 17th century on concepts of gravity, spinning of the earth and its rotation around the sun. The telescope and microscope opened enormous extensions of observations of what could be studied. As might be expected the establishment was concerned by and was hostile to the new developments. Machiavelli in "The Prince" published in 1513, certainly recognised the danger of these ideas.

"And let it be noted that there is no more delicate matter to take in hand, nor more dangerous to conduct, nor more doubtful in its success, than to set up as a leader in the introduction of changes. For he who innovates will have for his enemies all those who are well off under the existing order of things, and only the lukewarm supporters in those who might be better off under the new. This lukewarm temper arises partly from the fear of adversaries who have the laws on their side and partly from the incredulity of mankind, who will never admit the merit of anything new, until they have seen it proved by the event."

In 1600 the Inquisition burned the priest Bruno at the stake for a number of alleged heresies including suggesting that Copernicus was correct in postulating that the earth was not the centre of the Universe. Galileo was lucky to escape with prolonged house arrest in 1632 for his views and arguments confirming the Copernican hypothesis. Nevertheless the coercive power of the Catholic Church over the 17th and 18th centuries was not consistent in its opposition to new ideas and from time to time the hierarchy allowed the new thinkers to have breathing space. The scholarship, philosophical and artistic background of Ancient Greece were recorded in texts scattered in the Levant and many suffered damage in the fire of the great library of Alexandria. Scholars working for the Arab Caliphate rescued important early Greek texts and preserved them for posterity. The printing press, like gunpowder, a Chinese invention, allowed the dissemination of knowledge to spread throughout Europe. In the 17th Century in England men curious of nature met in coffee houses in London and eventually formed a Society to study natural knowledge. This became the Royal Society under the patronage of King Charles II and was the first of many scientific academies. Some powerful figures were sceptical of its early scientific efforts and critical of the uselessness of its endeavours and the infant society had difficulties in surviving let alone flourishing for a long time.

During the 18th and 19th centuries applications of new science led to the Industrial Revolution with a leap forward in the quality of life for the emerging middle classes in Western nations. Electricity illuminated the night in a predictable and effective way and required study and experimentation in understanding as to how it could be applied before the telegraph, wireless and telephones could be established. The harnessing of steam was developed into a reciprocating machine that drove powerful engines to be employed, first as static "workhorses" and then to revolutionise transport, with railways on land and steamships at sea, no longer at the mercy of the wiles of the wind. Internal combustion engines were modified into powerful mobile engines for cars and were essential to the invention in the 20th century of powered flight, pioneered by the Wright brothers in America (Figure 9). Improvements in efficiency and power were continuously added to make the speed and safety of air and land travel a universal and essential ingredient of contemporary civilisation.

Figure 9. The first flight of a powered aircraft by the Wright brothers 1902. The plane flew for twelve seconds. Orville at the controls while Wilbur watches anxiously.

An alternative to reciprocating engines was the invention of continuously rotating turbines which gave improved power and reliability. The concept was utilised in jet engines for aircraft which have now an extraordinary long life of trouble-free service. These immense advances were used for the improvement of the quality of life of many humans living in peace, but when conflict arose they were quickly utilised for improving the killing potential of new weapons. Ironclad warships and fighter airplanes are important examples of the new killing techniques.

WHO WERE THE INVENTORS OF MACHINES AND ENGINES?

Embarking on a sea voyage, navigating by dead reckoning with the help of the sun, the stars and a compass was an extremely hazardous undertaking before the longitude could be determined accurately. No wonder the mariners required a daily rum ration to keep their spirits up, since the hazard of shipwreck was very real and it was quite an accomplishment to complete a journey safely. The problem to be solved was clearly defined, how to determine the longitude during a voyage?

Most inventions resulted from the hard work and flashes of genius of curious and determined men and women who were aware of the tide of common knowledge and its progress and identified the possibilities of constructing and developing a new concept. It is often difficult to determine who was the prime mover in many of the great inventions, because frequently a number of scientists and inventors were moving towards the same objective from a similar background of knowledge. In a way it could be regarded as analogous to a pack of hounds chasing after a fox that they knew was somewhere, but one or two hounds smelt, saw, or heard the fox before the rest, and could be credited with the initiation of the success of the chase. Surges in knowledge will open up new areas for scientific hunting – the first half of the 20th century presented rich pickings for atomic and subatomic physics. Spectacular advances in the inventions and developments arising from this new physics revolution provided biochemists with tools to unravel cell and molecular biology which continues to be a happy hunting ground for scientists. Some inventions are shrouded in mystery and this applies to the magnetic compass, which was certainly known to the Chinese in the Han dynasty more than 200 years BC. The principle depended upon magnetic iron ore or lodestone, which if suspended or poised so that it could move freely, would align itself to the magnetic field of the earth and indicate north and south. Its use in navigation gave mariners an important reference point as a guide, but this valuable tool could not provide sufficient information for a safe voyage. The captain and navigator had to rely on land sightings, the sun and stars and estimate the winds and known currents and luck, especially the latter. Although avian migration has been studied extensively it is still amazing how accurate is the navigation of birds over hundreds or even thousands of miles. They have a magnetic and visual sensory apparatus that is extraordinarily precise and not by any means fully understood.

DETERMINATION OF THE LATITUDE AND LONGITUDE

There were two main clues to determining the latitude, one was the movement of the ship in relation to the sun and the other the Polaris star in the northern hemisphere. The accuracy of the information was greatly improved by the invention in the 18th century of the sextant which could determine the angle between the sun at noon and the horizon. At night the Pole star in the northern hemisphere would also be a sighting point for the sextant. Measurement of longitude had extra difficulties compared with determining the latitude. The latitude has a natural reference or starting point, the Equator, but longitude required an artificial meridian which by international agreement went through Greenwich in London on a curved line from North to South Pole. It was however extremely difficult to get an exact recording of longitude until an exceptionally accurate and robust clock was invented. In view of the numerous disasters at sea due to the inaccurate assessment of the position of ships, the British government offered a prize to the first person to demonstrate a practical method of determining the longitude of a ship at sea. John Harrison was a self-educated English clockmaker with an enormous experience in constructing accurate clocks and watches. He set himself the task of winning the prize. To determine the longitude it was necessary to have an accurate clock that recorded the time at the Greenwich meridian and then the time shown by the position of the sun from the ship at sea would allow calculation of the longitude from the difference between Greenwich time and the time on the ship. Dava Sobel recorded the story of the quest for the longitude prize. The tale is fascinating and involved much conniving, skulduggery and many failures as the winner had to produce a chronometer not only extremely accurate but also one that could withstand the buffeting that it would be subjected to during a storm at sea. Interestingly the prize had a sliding scale dependent upon how accurate the longitude determination would be, thus £10,000 for accuracy within 60 nautical miles, £15,000 for accuracy within 40 miles and £20,000 for accuracy within 30 nautical miles. John Harrison won after years of trial and error eventually received the award of £15,000, which at that time was an extremely valuable prize in monetary terms and fame but well deserved.

ELECTRICITY

Humans were aware of lightening and static electricity which were observed but not understood until the late 18th Century, when a distinction was made between magnetism in the lodestone and the electricity as a result of rubbing amber. There were exciting and original observations made in the late 18th and early 19th Centuries that provided the concept of flowing electric current and electro-magnetic induction, which gave rise to the electric motor and dynamo following pioneering work by James Maxwell. An electric current passing through a magnetic field results in the force that is used in electric motors, and this principle can be reversed so that a force could produce an electric current by the dynamo. One of the earliest important applications of electricity was to enable the binary Morse code to be transmitted along wires as telegrams. In the 1870s rich nations applied electricity to produce artificial lighting of far greater intensity and reliability than that produced by gas, oil lamps or candles. To have the availability of light for working and reading during the night had an enormous effect on human culture and behaviour. The invention of a workable telephone and the utilisation of radio waves and later television, were all responsible for huge changes in society and interaction between nations, and were readily applied to warfare. The names of Bell for the telephone, Marconi for radio and Baird for television are only three of many pioneers, who between them contributed to these major advances. There are many accounts of the history of these inventions, and the few names that are familiar are only part of a long and complicated story which would be inappropriate for consideration here.

POWER

The static reciprocating steam engine provided a new power source that once linked to a wheeled vehicle, blossomed into railways that revolutionised travel over land and were important drivers of the industrial revolution. There were several pioneers in these inventions and developments but James Watt's steam engine and George Stephenson's railway engine were significant practical achievements that really pushed forward the basic requirements for the Industrial Revolution to flourish. The linking of the steam engine to propel ships by paddles and then propellers, made a similar contribution to travel at sea and the reciprocating engine using internal combustion of fuel invented by Diesel and Daimler in Germany produced the modern automobile. The fuel was ignited by compression in diesel motors and by a controlled spark in petroleum engines. Although a major conceptual advance, reciprocating engines were at first not very efficient but improvements in design led to powerful and increasingly reliable car and aero-engines. The success of the automobile has been so great that now it is difficult to use the invention in big cities due to congestion, and with the eventual completion of the journey, where to park has become a formidable problem, sometimes impossible to solve.

An alternative concept was to harness the power to a continuously rotating wheel by the drive of fans, known as turbines. The steam turbine had great success in powering ships, (Figure 10 "Turbina" launched 1894) especially war ships and the jet turbine, in which fuel combustion occurred as part of the rotating mechanism, led to the jet engine which has been responsible for rapid and safe flights worldwide. The jet engine was invented and developed independently at the same time by Frank Whittle in the UK and Hans von Ohain in Germany. An entirely different form of energy was released from atomic fission and will be discussed later.

Figure 10. "Turbina" was the fastest ship in the world powered by steam turbine, able to do 34 knots in 1897.

MATERIALS DERIVED FROM SCIENCE

The ancient inhabitants of Mexico and other parts of Latin America practised a variety of ball games which were extremely important in their culture as a spectator sport, a religious ritual, exhibition of extreme skill and danger with an important element of gambling and dire consequences of losing, not dissimilar from modern football except the penalty of losing was to be sacrificed by decapitation or removal of the heart, rather more serious than the sacking of a football manager in contemporary culture! (Figure 11)

Figure 11. Aztec – ball game where the losing team loses all, including their hearts. The ball was made of natural polymer rubber.

The ball used was made of hard rubber and quite heavy, weighing around 9lbs. The objective was to negotiate the ball through a narrow ring, which was very difficult, but the stakes were high. The ball itself was derived from natural latex, which had many uses in the ancient Mesoamerican cultures but its toughness and especially its elasticity are properties which endure today in most ball games. Rubber is a natural polymer involving the linking together of numerous organic radicals and when it was discovered by Columbus and bought back to the West, various new uses were devised and the natural latex base was modified by a chemical reaction with sulphur which made the rubber more resilient, a process known as vulcanisation. The demand for rubber rapidly increased when its value in the construction of tyres for vehicles became apparent and shortage of rubber during war time was a powerful stimulus for scientists to devise a synthetic substitute. In this task they were very successful. The output of synthetic rubber derived from petroleum products now exceeds that from natural rubber trees grown in South East Asia. The uses of rubber in industry, medicine and household appliances are widespread and extremely valuable to modern civilisation.

Our world has now been transformed by materials loosely classified together as plastics. They are based on synthetic polymers derived from petroleum products. A cheap and important early plastic made from phenol and formaldehyde was invented by Hendrik Baekeland in New York in 1907 and was called "Bakelite", a widely used insulating material for wires to conduct electricity and in the construction of many electrical appliances.

Polystyrene was another cheap plastic which had many uses in the building industry and polyvinylchloride, known as PVC, had important properties for constructing tubes for drainage and general household plumbing and also for food packaging and waterproof garments.

"Nylon" is a fibre synthesized by the chemist Wallace Carothers working in the Du Pont corporation in 1935. The flexible and very strong nylon fibres became a serious competitor to silk, being much cheaper and therefore it had a mass market in the production of nylon stockings and other clothes which required a silk-like consistency. It could also be manufactured as a bristle for brushes. During the 2nd World War nylon became a war material in the manufacture of parachutes.

Roy Plunkett, also working for the Du Pont company in 1938, discovered by accident "Teflon", a material that resists corrosion and damage from heat. This non-stick property has entered the language with an additional meaning of somebody who seems to be immune to harm and any kind of corruption, or at least no evidence of corruption ever seems to 'stick'.

All these plastics have toxicity and a pollution effect, since they do not dissolve in water. They are littering all the oceans killing fish and plants by interfering with their habitats. Because of environmental worries there has been intense activity among scientists to find a way of degrading plastics or constructing a naturally biodegradable plastic. Huge amounts of fossil fuels are used to produce plastics. Some bacteria will degrade individual plastic compounds and methods of using bacteria for this purpose are being investigated on a commercial scale. Controlled disposal of plastics are improving so that those that can be reused by melting are not discarded as dangerous litter.

During the 2nd World War an extremely powerful glue, based on a resin and a catalyst called epoxy resin "Araldite" was developed to construct the Mosquito fighter bomber aircraft which was made of wood. These glues became important in the building industry and especially in assembling plastics in a stable and strong manner. So they are used in most of the applications of plastics and it is of interest that the war time use has nevertheless had an important spin-off in civilian constructions and all these materials are components of space exploration, rockets and space satellites. They will have further development with 3D printing which is now becoming affordable.

Carbon fibre is a form of reinforced plastic which is exceedingly strong and also very light. It has been used in sports equipment, especially skis and tennis rackets. It is an integral component in the construction of the huge passenger aircraft, the Boeing "Dreamliner". To have a much lighter material than aluminium with comparable strength is an advantage likely to be seized by many other aircraft companies.

A water-based acrylic resin was invented in Germany in the 1930s and has now become the basis of many industrial paints and is an excellent medium in fine art. The acrylic polymer provides a medium for adding dyes in the production of paints. The water-based materials become hardened and very resistant after exposure to air for a short time. Acrylics do not produce toxic fumes and are therefore becoming increasingly popular in general applications requiring a robust paint surface. They are excellent transparent substitutes for glass and other glass-like polymers.

From the DuPont laboratories in 1964 once again a new, strong and versatile material "Kevlar" was discovered by accident by the prepared mind of the chemist Stephanie Kwolek. Kevlar is a liquid crystal derived polymer with many applications that include reinforcing tyres, construction of body armour clothing, making wind turbines, ropes, brake linings, musical instruments, Smartphones and recently experimental electricity-generating material with zinc oxide nanowires woven into a fabric that might be used in a jacket that would light up and warm itself!

New materials that are at an early stage of development are Graphine and carbon nanotubes. Graphine is a one atom thick layer of carbon discovered in a manageable form by the Nobel prize winning physicists Andre Geim and Kostya Novoselov, working in Manchester University. They were aware of the remarkable properties of a single layer of carbon atoms forming a two dimensional lattice, but they had difficulty in studying it until they were successful in obtaining a sheet of graphine adhering to "Sellotape", which they had applied to graphite to clean it before using it in the laboratory. This serendipitous discovery has created great interest since graphine is a remarkable conductor of electricity; it is light, transparent and very strong.

Carbon nanotubes are exceedingly strong graphine tubes produced from graphite. Different varieties of nanotube each with individual properties are now being developed. Both graphine sheets and nanotubes will probably be used in numerous applications including the next generation of computers, working on quantum physical principles.

So scientific discoveries deliberately probed and developed by curious minds and also a result of serendipity, have transformed almost every activity with which we are involved, mostly to improve the quality of life, but with spin-offs identified that have destructive potential.

SCIENCE AND FOOD - THE GREEN REVOLUTION

The impact of science on food production has been enormous. In the mid-20th century with the huge rise in population food shortages occurred with famine in a number of countries and there was great concern as to how to feed this increasing number of human-beings. In Mexico and later in India the so-called "Green Revolution" began with the introduction of totally new strains of wheat, rice and maize. The father figure of this Green Revolution was Norman Borlaug, an American plant biologist who changed the whole scene of pending disaster to one of success and optimism.

It is interesting that Gregor Mendel in his classical plant experiments used a short stemmed strain of bean with a genetic makeup of a clear cut mathematical inheritance pattern according to Mendel's laws. Borlaug introduced the idea of developing food plants with an investment in the edible seed part of the plant instead of the stem, so the objective was to produce strains with high yield and short stems. An additional advantage of the short stem would be less likelihood of the plant keeling over by the weight of the high yield seeds and the wind.

Plants require nitrogen in a form that they can metabolise. Bacteria living in the root nodules of leguminous plants, for example peas, beans and clover, can fix nitrogen from the air in a form that can nourish the plants but most edible crops do not have this facility and rely on manure and other natural fertilizers which could not meet the demand of the rising human population.

"The Green Revolution" was preceded by the invention of a process to produce artificial fertilizers on an industrial scale involving the conversion of nitrogen in the air and hydrogen from natural gas into ammonia, which was the basis of the new synthetic fertilizers. The process was invented by Fritz Haber, a German chemist whose laboratory experiments were translated into a commercial industrial manufacturing plant using iron based catalysts introduced by his colleague Karl Bosch. There has been a massive development of artificial fertilizers incorporating many minerals, but especially phosphorous and potassium. Probably more than a third of the world's population, previously faced with starvation, have been saved indirectly due to the Haber-Bosch process to produce artificial fertilizers. Interestingly in sympathy with the title of this book, during the first World War the process was also used to produce ammonia for explosives manufacture. So once again a process devised primarily to help humanity was seized on and used by politicians to sustain war efforts and enhance lethal consequences. . Fritz Haber subsequently developed poison gas and was active in its use in World War I. His wife was so distressed by his work on poison gas as a weapon that she committed suicide, shooting herself with his service pistol. Fritz Haber's contribution to avoiding famine for millions nevertheless later led to him poisoning thousands and was an example of deliberate use of science to produce lethal weapons.

The availability of artificial fertilizers worldwide and the extremely clever use of inbreeding to select species with appropriate advantages to be grown in different parts of the world, has greatly eased the pressure on the real risk of worldwide famine and indirectly has been responsible for a major increase in population, since without the new food availability, millions of people in poor countries would have starved. Of course the artificial fertilizers have side effects. They require energy to produce and therefore will contribute to carbon release and probably global warming. The fertilizers themselves can seep into the soil and ground-water and many of them are toxic to fish and aquatic plants. Some may also increase the risk of cancer in humans and animals.

The next stage in improving world food supplies will be to develop crops genetically modified by direct molecular biological engineering. This has been a major endeavour in a number of companies particularly by the Monsanto corporation in America which has a huge global commercial interest.

Genetically modified crops may have different characteristics but pests and infection resistance are the main features that have so far been exploited. The taste of food can be altered by genetic modification and also ability to withstand storage in good condition longer than using traditional crops. The use of GM food-producing plants has not shown any evidence of disease or disability in humans or animals, but there have been widespread fears voiced and the agricultural ecology of plants will certainly be influenced if the pests do not reproduce in their natural manner. In North America GM foods have been widely accepted by the population and this is also true in some developing countries. In Europe GM foods have been opposed vociferously and irrationally by pressure groups who have even destroyed crops and indirectly interfered with the feeding of poor people on the verge of famine. These European behavioural anomalies are unlikely to prevent development of genetically modified crops which would seem to have almost unlimited potential unless there is a completely unexpected disaster.

Recently laboratory cultured muscle cells produced a material that had some resemblance to meat but the expressions on the faces of politicians tucking into the cultured hamburgers made one a little sceptical that beef farming was about to be superseded.

So besides the hijacking of scientific advances to produce new weapons, science in the food chain has been and will continue to be a major influence in population growth and indirectly the depletion of food and water resources and pollution of the air contributing to global warming. This unfortunate aspect has been a result of what otherwise has been claimed as a miracle for human welfare. The consequences of science are always difficult and often impossible to predict.

OBSERVATIONS DIFFICULT TO UNDERSTAND - TECTONICS

God does not play dice with the Universe

Albert Einstein

Irrespective of the theological implications, in the case of subatomic physics Einstein got it wrong that time in his correspondence with Max Born. Statistical consistency is a feature of observations of the behaviour of subatomic particles in a quantum environment but this behaviour is individually unpredictable and would appear to have much in common with the chance of predicting numbers to be revealed on throwing a dice. The chances of a "6" appearing can be accurately determined statistically but this does not help advising one how to bet on an individual throw. This pattern of phenomena being capable of study and analysis in a statistical manner but lacking in individual predictive ability is a feature of observations on many natural events.

Aristotle (384-322BC), the pupil of Plato and teacher of Alexander the Great, was an extraordinary polymath who turned his inquisitive and exceptionally brilliant mind to all the important unsolved questions that he came across, from philosophy, mathematics, astronomy and biology. He made careful and accurate observations and analysis within the limits of the tools available at that time and the established knowledge from previous generations. His perception and hypotheses on each of the subjects he addressed were graced with a brilliance and persuasiveness that led to him being regarded as a fountain of knowledge that could not be argued against. This iconic status persisted into the Christian era and was adopted by the Church, so Aristotle's observations became a sacred canon and any opposing theories were regarded as heresy. This made it very difficult for subsequent scientists because, brilliant though he was, Aristotle could only make observations through facilities and instruments to which he had access. So when the Renaissance began to flourish in the 16th and 17th centuries the prime movers were always in fear of the long arm of Aristotle adopted by the Papacy with its elaborate, powerful and cruel 'Inquisition'.

Greek mathematics and geometry formed the backbone and whole skeleton of modern science. It provided the medium of numerical measurement of new observations and these could be repeated by separate individuals and gave powerful credence to hypotheses. Nevertheless observations with conflicting interpretations continually erupt in science. Though further experiments may or may not clarify the confusion and sort out the differences, what we know and what we think we know have always troubled philosophers since, and probably before, Plato. Observations with new instruments, especially the telescope and microscope provided overwhelming evidence that the old axioms of Aristotle were often in error, especially in biological matters but also in concepts of astronomy. The new scientists of the Renaissance had to tread delicately otherwise they were in danger of vicious persecution. In the 19th century a number of facts were established and the evidence from the observations and new concepts could not be dismissed.

Traditionally mystical or religious explanations had often been accepted, but they were not compatible with new scientific evidence. Thus early geologists had found seashells and fish fossils in rocks high in the mountains and each generation was faced with compelling evidence of the earth's age being far in excess of that laid down in the Bible. When mariners started exploring the world they discovered strange creatures in far-off lands, particularly in Australia and New Zealand where a whole major category of animals was found that nurtured their offspring in pouches, the marsupials. In Africa also strange creatures were encountered and tales of these findings were relayed home when the mariners and explorers returned and were received with either scepticism or awe and amazement. The famous animal painter, Stubbs, produced a wonderful image of a giraffe, a creature he had never seen.

Gradually an interesting puzzle presented itself; how could it be that these completely different animals and plants were encountered in far-off places? When maps were drawn there seemed to be an obvious relationship between the bulge of the west coast of Africa and the contours of the east coast of South America. It looked as if there might have been a fitting together of these two continents but what had happened? That was the question that could not easily be answered. Gradually concepts of the shifting of continents westward, the "continental drift", was postulated, based on the idea that once there was a single enormous landmass surrounded by sea but this fragmented and the pieces moved apart to explain the observed geographical contours and the similarities of the displaced plants and animals in some situations, whereas there was a wide disparity in others. All this pointed to a huge length of time scale that was involved in this process and a very slow movement of the continental masses as they separated from each other.

The existence of volcanoes and hot springs pointed to tremendous heat in the depths of the planet and when volcanoes erupted the material that was thrown out gave a clue as to what existed in the depths but did not provide evidence of how uniform and fluid was molten heated lava. Devastating earthquakes occurred in different parts of the world, suggesting fracturing of the terrestrial crust superficial to the hot molten deep mantle. The continental rifts, volcanic and earthquake-prone areas could be mapped out and gradually a story appeared which seemed to fit some of the facts. No one person seemed to be responsible for the theory but much of the bewildering observations could be explained if the breakup of the original single world continental mass resulted in a few huge continental tectonic plates. Then if these were moving, albeit very slowly in relation to each other, they might separate or come together in boundary zones and then, if they were floating on a molten mantle, it could be imagined that they might in certain situations of contact cause upward pressure of the earth's crust and explain the formation of the highest mountains on earth and also how fossils of sea creatures came to reside in the high levels of mountainous territory. The other category of mountains is the result of volcanoes. What caused the tectonic plates to move has been the subject of controversy and is still not entirely settled. Theories have been suggested that include convection currents in the mantle, stretching of the seabed, centrifugal force of the spinning of the earth, the effects of tides and gravity. There is a consensus that when the plates collide, one may submerge below the other which is believed to have happened in North America. Alternatively the plates could move apart. It is thought that there are probably eight huge continental plates and many smaller ones making the whole picture very confused and not fully mapped. Nevertheless the concept of plate tectonics is now accepted, although the details still arouse great controversy amongst scientists who have devoted their lives to study of this subject. Of course this is of much more than just theoretical interest, since prediction of earthquakes and volcanic eruptions would be of enormous value to warn populations to move away from the dangerous zones. This might have saved the inhabitants of Pompeii and Herculaneum who were annihilated by the massive explosion of Vesuvius in AD79. If an earthquake occurs under the sea, a devastating sea wave or tsunami can travel with disastrous effects thousands of miles away from the centre of the earthquake, behaving in a manner that is difficult to foretell depending on the severity of the disturbance, and its depth in the sea and the geography of the surrounding seabed and shoreline. Shaking of the earth can be recorded by sensitive seismographs, once again based on an invention of the ancient Chinese. There is now worldwide monitoring of seismographic activity by satellites. This complicated and extensive network of surveillance was established to police any testing of atomic weapons that would break treaties and agreements. Together with multiple tsunami monitoring floats in the oceans of the world, we have an elaborate international organisation that can give warning of the likely propagation of a tsunami. Unfortunately so far the ability to predict earthquakes is still very unsatisfactory although some warning signs can be picked up and there may be rumbling activity in volcanoes preceding a major eruption in time for threatened populations to be evacuated. The relationship of mining, dam building and fracking to the occurrence of earthquakes is currently being studied.

We now have reasonable explanations of the difficult questions that faced our 19th century ancestors but understanding is still far from complete so there remains much work to be done and no doubt a great deal of controversy will continue in the process of unraveling the mysteries that persist.

CHINESE INVENTIONS

The inventive success in ancient China was well ahead of Western and Middle Eastern efforts but was not supported by a philosophical and mathematical scholarship comparable to that of the ancient Greeks. Chinese inventions were each appropriated or at least further developed in an advantageous manner by Western and Islamic nations. The surge forward of science following the Renaissance in the 16th and 17th centuries was possible because of the invention of new instruments that were capable of scientific measurements, especially the telescope and the microscope. The demonstration of the circulation of the blood and an understanding of the scientific method resulted in an escalation of new knowledge of the natural world. At this period the Chinese politics were inward-looking and isolationist. Since then scientific advances including the development of new weapons have flourished in the West and China has for the most part played "catch-up" activity without marked innovation.

It is not easy to understand why this gap between China and the West occurred. Two factors may be relevant, first the Chinese written language based on ideograms was used by eminent scholars almost as a lifetime occupation in memorising thousands of different ideograms without leaving much time or ambition for other activities. Second, Chinese mathematics were complicated, based on the abacus, while in the West the alphabetical languages of the Middle East, Greece and Rome together with Arabic numerals, helped in the expression of new scientific concepts and the working out of complicated mathematical problems which were relevant to the new inventions being developed in Western nations. Perhaps another factor of importance was the hierarchical nature of all Chinese cultures, excluding dissent and discouraging discourse and constructive criticism. Not that these features were abundant in Western culture but from time to time in the West the Church and government did allow space for new ideas to be discussed, especially if the rulers were interested in the subject and thought they might understand and even contribute to the scientific revolution.

EXPLOSIVES

The origins of gunpowder are obscure but they seem to be derived from legends concerning the Chinese man-eating monster "Nian" (Figure 12), which terrified lonely people but apparently could be scared away by loud noise. Sitting round a wood fire some

Figure 12. Nian – Chinese mythical man-eating creature that lived in the mountains and the sea. Was part lion, part unicorn, part dragon. It was terrified by noise and the colour red. Features in Chinese New Year ceremonies (RYC).

Chinese peasants were warming themselves and added bamboo sticks, some of which when heated by the flames exploded with a loud and frightening noise. This was due to the closed cylinder between nodes of bamboo and the strength of the bamboo cylinder so that the air heated in the fire reached a high pressure before it ruptured the bamboo wall. The noise frightened people and animals and presumably also scared away the Nian, and these fire crackers became useful protectors from evil and essential in celebrations, still important in modern Chinese New Year festivities. The significance of mythological creatures in Chinese culture is immediately apparent on a visit to Hong Kong, where many modern buildings have large gaps in their design decreed by "Feng shui" soothsayer experts. It is believed to be an important requirement for good fortune to placate dragons which live in the hills at the summit of Hong Kong island, so that they can fly directly through the gaps in the buildings to the sea without being hampered by the need to negotiate high buildings.

Probably by accident in the 9th century AD Chinese alchemists found the recipe for a form of gunpowder in which saltpetre, sulphur and carbon charcoal were the main ingredients. This explosive mixture when inserted into the hollow of a bamboo branch and then heated on a fire produced a much louder bang than that resulting from air alone. The new super firecrackers were soon perceived by the military as potential instruments of war and when a fuse was lit at one end, the exploding bamboo arrows would shoot all over the place, like wild rats and cause terror not only to opponents but also to the artillery men (Figure 13). When fins were fitted at the back of the tube the weapon could be directed with some accuracy and in fact this was the first use of rockets which could act as celebratory fireworks in a spectacle or be modified into lethal weapons. The Chinese also made gunpowder or black powder bombs that could be projected with slings or dropped on enemy fortifications. Early cannons were constructed out of bamboo tubes by the Chinese and modified by Islamic and Western nations into metal-based cylindrical cannons used in battles in the 14th and 15th centuries, notably in the Siege of Orleans (Figure 14) and the Battle of Crecy by British troops.

Chinese soldier launches fire-arrow

Figure 13. Chinese artillery soldier launches a fire arrow.

Refinement of explosives occurred intermittently. A mixture of concentrated nitric and sulphuric acids led to the invention of nitro-glycerine in the mid-nineteenth century. This was an extremely dangerous liquid prone to accidental detonation. Alfred Nobel, the founder of the Nobel Prizes, invented a derivative of nitro-glycerine, called dynamite, which was more manageable and had widespread use both in civilian application, for building roads and railways, and also as explosive weapons, powerful enough to penetrate thick steel armour. Cordite, a smokeless explosive was widely used in bullet and shell cartridges. A flaming adherent chemical linked to incendiary "napalm" bombs produced terrible burns in victims in the Vietnam war and also recently in the Syrian civil war. Explosives have also been used to disseminate chemical weapons and they are required to initiate the detonation of thermonuclear devices in atom bombs. Semtex is a plastic explosive with industrial use in blasting and also military applications. It has been popular with terrorists as it is difficult to detect. "Fertilizer bombs" based on the plant nutrient ammonium nitrate is a cheap, easily obtained "do it yourself" explosive also attractive to terrorists.

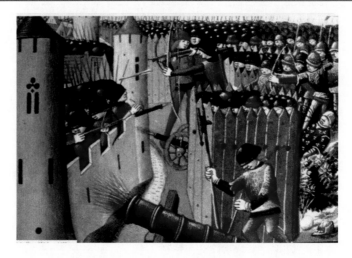

Figure 14. The Siege of Orleans showing metal cannon in action.

So the initial discovery of a method of frightening away the evil man-eating Nian, evolved into the most destructive killing weapons.

Alfred Nobel's brother Ludvig was killed in an accidental explosion and this personal tragedy, together with his realisation of the dreadful invention he had brought into the world, are thought to have persuaded him to leave a the legacy of the Nobel Prizes as a gift to humanity from his huge fortune.

DISSEMINATION OF KNOWLEDGE

The flow of knowledge from person to person and generation to generation is needed for it to be fully utilised and word of mouth is an inefficient medium for this process. A permanent record is required that can be consulted by scholars separated in space and time. The earliest records were made by writing with incisions into wet clay or carving on to the surface of stones, bones or other suitable material. To provide many copies would be an obvious advantage and the first attempts at multiple copying were in the form of stamps pressed into soft clay or covered with a pigment which acted as an ink. An advance on flat stamps was to use an engraved roller which produced some very beautiful, early multiple copies dating back to civilisations in Mesopotamia around 3000 BC. In ancient cultures of China and Egypt stamps were used of varying sizes and were modified to print designs on cloth, particularly silk. With the development of paper in China and papyrus in Egypt new possibilities arose for inventions that would allow multiple copies. The words and/or designs were cut into wood blocks which then were inked and pressed on to paper. Examples exist from China going back to around 200 BC during the Han dynasty. The importance of spreading religious texts was emphasised by Buddhist scholars in China and every religion has sought to disseminate its creed and exhort and frighten its followers with multiple copies of sacred texts.

Movable type was developed in SE Asia and especially in Korea. In Europe the process was adopted later and a "game change" occurred in the German City of Mainz where Johannes Gutenberg developed metallic movable type, oil-based ink and printers' metal, a mixture of lead, tin and antimony. The Gutenberg Bible was published in 1455 and the mass distribution of sacred books was instrumental in the spread of both Christianity and Islam. An important and powerful political dogma followed the publication of the secular treatise *Das Capital* by Karl Marx, the "Bible of Communism". Throughout history books have been used to spread ideas including psychological manipulation to establish beliefs and increase prejudice. Often tales of miracles enhance successful religious publications, strangely without undermining credulity, and may even reinforce beliefs.

During the 16th and 17th centuries there was an extraordinary constellation of brilliant thinkers and mathematicians in Europe who published books that revolutionised our approach to the world. The physician, mathematician and astronomer Copernicus challenged the Aristotelian belief, that our world was all important to the concept that the earth revolved round the sun. The idea that the earth was not the centre of the Universe was a dangerous proposition as far as the Church hierarchy was concerned. Copernicus's book on the revolution of asteroid spheres was published the day he died so he escaped the possible attentions of the Inquisition, which caught up with Galileo who was lucky to escape with his life, although condemned to perpetual house arrest. Newton and Kepler avoided serious harassment possibly because their contributions were mainly mathematical and therefore difficult for the non-specialist to understand.

In the mid-19th century Darwin, Wallace and Mendel contributed to a complete reassessment of how plants and animals evolved and the relationship between the earliest forms of life and those that followed. The publication of *The Origin of the Species* was delayed by Darwin for 20 years because he was fearful of persecution from the Church. It was only when he was aware that Alfred Wallace had arrived independently at the same basic conclusion concerning evolution, that both Darwin and Wallace presented papers *in absentia* to the Linnean Society in London in 1858. Mendel's light was hidden under a bushel for much longer. His breeding and cross-breeding experiments with plants, many of which were conducted in the monastery where Mendel was the Abbot, provided a mathematical basis for the whole process of inheritance and the relationship between the genotype and phenotype of individual living organisms, described by Mendel in the only paper he ever published. Mendel would have no chance of obtaining a grant to pursue his studies nowadays with such a scant publication list and he worked in relative obscurity. His golden nugget of knowledge would have been seized gratefully by Darwin to reinforce his theories. It is alleged that a journal referring to Mendel's paper was on a shelf in Darwin's private library, but the significant pages had not been cut, a lesson in the importance of disseminating knowledge but also of paying attention to what is published! Even in Darwin's time not everything could be read and digested, especially a paper in a rather obscure journal.

So the value and exponential rise in the amount of printed material developed with new improved mechanics of printing succeeded each other in rapid sequence. Printing on long continuous rolls of paper was possible with the invention of the rotary printing press in the mid-19th century. A variety of colour printing techniques were invented and some were adapted successfully in fine art applications. The photocopier, laser and ink jet printers have transferred the production of multiple copies to normal offices throughout the world. Unfortunately they have not succeeded in the aim of producing paperless offices. In fact the ease of printing seems to have increased the use of paper. The digital transfer of information from the computer to the printed text is now remarkably easy and the quality of printing in black and white and colour has steadily improved, and has also been utilised for providing high quality reproductions of art work.

The applications and development of printing have had an enormous effect on civilisation, in religious and political matters, and has changed the way business is transacted between individuals, especially allowing instantaneous transmission of information which can be converted into trans-continental dialogue, in text, sound and televised intercourse. It is possible to set up a virtual person-to-person contact, although this is still not the same thing as speaking to a person and looking into their eyes. All these advances have had good and potentially harmful effects and with the increasing popularity of 3D printers, there will be a proliferation of this new medium which has also the possibility of sinister ramifications.

HISTORY OF THE COMPUTER

The first serious attempt to create a machine which could compute mathematical solutions to problems that would be difficult to solve by hand was tackled by Charles Babbage in the early 19th Century. It was a very complicated clockwork machine which was expensive and technically difficult to make with the materials and tools available to Babbage who failed to construct his machine. It has recently been shown that if it had been assembled using modern materials and techniques it would have worked, as the principles involved were correct. It was a remarkable achievement before its time but the help of electricity was needed to make a reliable useful computer. There were a number of far-sighted and innovative mathematicians who might share the role of "father of the modern computer" but there were several crucial stages on the way to our current use of computers, desktop, laptop, tablets and smart phones, not to mention intrinsic components of cars, aeroplanes and ships. An important step was to agree on a computer language of binary figures consisting of variations of the sequence 0 and 1 and substitution of the gas-filled valve for a transistor. The huge size of the early computers filling one or more rooms was rapidly whittled down to what we know today and will, no doubt become even smaller when digital quantum computers are developed. The usefulness of the computer depended on the speed with which it accomplished its tasks, and the provision of an enormous, almost unending memory. When computers were linked together electronically by wire and wireless, to form an "internet" these features were greatly enhanced. Although the developing computers were initially conceived and used as tools for research scientists, the days of secrecy and exclusivity were soon opened up for everyone as the World Wide Web invented by Tim Berners-Lee.

The practical use of the early valve computers during the 2nd World War gave the allies important strategic information harvested by a group of academic mathematicians working in Bletchley in England and notably influenced by Alan Turing. His first machine was electromechanical, which morphed into the first programmable computer "the Colossus". This was a demonstration of how a government-planned secret institute for scientists could be successful in coming up with the goods. The increasing complexity of computers left loopholes for their sabotage by malicious but clever amateurs or as a concerted programme of spying and infiltration by nations and companies. In 1947 the first identified saboteur was in fact a moth discovered by Grace Hopper, an American programmer, which was trapped in an early Harvard mark II computer, giving the name "bug" for this type of computer disruption and other malware agents were identified as worms, Trojan horses and viruses, characterized by the way in which their harmful messages can be reproduced and spread. Gordon Moore in 1965 predicted that the number of transistors on integrated circuits would double approximately every two years and this prediction has so far been observed in practice (Moore's Law). We do not know how long this rate of acceleration can continue but the speed of change has been impressive.

There have been reports that the introduction of computers has reduced productivity in the workplace due to the temptation to use the computer unnecessarily and also for activities not related to company work.

This short summary of some of the historical background illustrates how each advance in knowledge could be exploited at times of conflict to produce more deadly weapons and this acceleration in new weapon development occurred at increasing speed during the 20th century, culminating in the use of atomic energy to kill hundreds of thousands of people with two bombs and the harnessing of the same source of energy to produce power for peaceful uses. Some of the new categories of weapons will be considered in subsequent chapters.

Chapter III

HUMAN NATURE

The nature of human beliefs and behaviour are inexorably woven into the culture that is encouraged, enforced and taught in every community. Each of the main religions has a story of its foundation and relationship with its god or gods and how the religious doctrine evolving by miraculous, supernatural means has forged ritual into the orthodox religions with ramifications extending into secular laws, family life and civil behaviour. It would be attractive to assume an optimistic appraisal of human nature, as the Harvard Professor, Stephen Pinker has strongly argued in his book "Better Angels of our nature" in which he traces changes in human nature evolving over the course of recorded history with a general trend towards less aggressive tendencies. However human behaviour is partially governed by the indisputable link to the genetic material with which we are born. Within a family there is a natural love, best shown between mother and child but also with the father and larger extensions of the family. The tribal society ensures that children behave according to the prevailing culture. Each individual needs enough to eat, drink and to keep warm and above all other considerations the ability to find a mate to reproduce, without which the species will perish. There is a basic natural aggression directed towards anything and anyone interfering with these essential requirements. Violence has been a central player in the acquisition and maintenance of territorial possession. Many species, including *Homo sapiens*, are inclined to competition and violent confrontation, especially in seeking a suitable mate. (Cock fighting Figure 15.)

Cock Fight

Quest for a Mate

Figure 15. Cockfight to the death. The winner's reward is the hen. Male rivalry a common feature in animal life (RYC).

Interpretation of religious doctrines has been the declared reason of wars throughout recorded history. There have been recurrent urges to go to war, often fuelled by nations' hawk-like ambitions, not based on any real threat. An Iraqi lady interviewed by the BBC lamented "how could hatred of one man justify destruction of a whole nation?". The alleged possession of weapons of mass destruction by Sadam Hussein was the *"casus belli"* in sympathy with the cynical recommendation of Otto von Bismarck "never believe anything until it is officially denied". Sometimes the doctrinal differences between religions are hard to understand by those looking on from outside. The imposing of religious law on all members can be loosely applied, for example, in Buddhism, or in other religions enforced by extreme and murderous violence imposed on those who stray from the prescribed path.

Despite a desire for optimism, the facts show a varying picture at different times and in different places. The civil war in Syria has resulted in more than 100,000 deaths in two years, many of the victims being women and children. Poison gas has been used on civilians and the bodies of enemies are mutilated and internal organs have been publically eaten. Children have been coerced to take up arms and forced to murder and torture as demonstrated with barbarous, almost unbelievable evil callousness in the ordering of a child of 12 to sever the head of a helpless prisoner. The dangers of violence and vengeance of conflict tend to spiral upwards in an escalation often encouraged and aided by outside powers with separate agendas who wish to spread the war for their own advantage. A civil war begun to usurp a dictatorship in favour of a democracy has degenerated into a tribal war of religion with Sunni versus Shia and Alawite and with Christians persecuted by all.

Whether or not human nature has improved and people are more loving towards one another and less inclined to criminality and violence, there is certainly no shortage of these vices in most parts of the world. When in London in 2011 the police were taken by surprise in a violent street confrontation, the impotence of normal police control was swiftly apparent to the protestors who set on a wave of intimidation, theft, destruction and arson, which gathered momentum with amazing rapidity aided by social networking on the internet and spread to other cities besides London. In 1969 police officers and fire fighters went on strike in Montreal and all mayhem of violent crime rapidly escalated in a city that had prided itself on its civility and low crime rates. Alcohol, drugs and poverty interact to fuel an underclass in most Western countries, where individuals seem to have lost hope in making a positive contribution to a civilised society. Jobs are scarce, unemployment high and the peoples' mood can behave like a tinderbox bursting into flames as occurred in the countries involved in the "Arab Spring", which started in Tunisia with the gesture of a poor young man, Mohamed Bouazizi, who set himself on fire as a protest against a tyrannical regime that had arbitrarily taken away his modest street vending livelihood that he and his large family depended upon to be fed The application of science contributed to the extent and success of the uprisings. The cell phone and the internet allowed instant mass communication, not only exhorting people to protest, but also co-ordinating them to where and how this protest would take place. The focus of blame was on a leader, the government in general or the whole of society.

The authorities tend to adopt a special language in trying to absolve themselves of blame when something goes wrong. The explanation that politicians, military leaders and executives give when challenged is often a mixture of irony and obfuscation. This language of "politico-bureau-speak" can be quickly decoded after it has been used repeatedly to explain something that has failed and will probably not be put right. Thus if bereaved relatives claim that in the past year there have been a 100 unnecessary local hospital deaths in the elderly, who had been abused verbally, physically, starved, denied fluids and left lying in faeces and urine, then a democratic challenge through the media is likely to be defended by the politician or executive in charge by saying:

1. "We take these allegations very seriously",
2. "We will set up a thorough investigation",
3. "We will prepare a report that is fully transparent and there will be a complete change in the culture and organisation of the hospital".

The rising number of sceptics will interpret these excuses as follows:

1. "We take seriously", equals – we have shredded the files and destroyed the hard drives.
2. "We will instigate a thorough investigation" – wait until I find the slimy bastard who blew the whistle
3. "Transparency" – we will make opaque all the windows so you will not have any idea of what went on and what is going on.

The phrase "to be honest" relating to a policy, suggests that previous policies have been dishonest and that the individual who now claims to be honest really means that "I am about to lie" or has lied already and the "thorough change" promised means "I will remain in charge and get rid of the underlings I do not like".

The internet, cell phone and recording of personal details and conversations, often covertly, all result from the application of science. It may be easier for individuals to protest but depending on the government their complaints may be accepted or brutally suppressed.

The above discussion would suggest that there may be little evidence in favour of basic change in human nature but society, culture and religion can influence human nature in a variety of different ways and lead to peaceful, civilised co-existence or the reverse. These observations apply to humans nature in general but in any society there will always be some individuals who deviate from the natural history of human behaviour and these individuals may coalesce in quasi-religious sects bent on causing disruption, damage, injury and death to other citizens, who are taken by surprise and totally unprepared for the active expression of such violent hatred.

HUMAN NATURE AND SCIENCE

The Bible and Shakespeare provide beautiful and poetic treatises on human nature covering love, altruism, co-operation, jealousy, rage, revenge, murder, lust, curiosity and power. Humans can believe almost anything depending on the presentation. Francis Bacon expressed the concept of "knowledge is power". The meaning of the word "science" as knowledge is discussed in various contexts in this book. Historically our knowledge base has been established from observations, experience and learning from mistakes and lucky successful actions. Observations of the natural world initially were interpreted in a commonsense manner that the earth as we know it is flat and that the sun rises each day in the east and sets in the west. It took many centuries before the discrepancies in this "received wisdom" could not be ignored and the spherical nature of the earth was established and accepted, not least because mariners could circumnavigate the globe, travelling in one direction and ending up where they began.

There was strong religious belief that the earth was the centre of the Universe as decreed by Aristotle and it took many years of observation, argument, discussion and intellectual conflict before the heliocentric theory of Copernicus was accepted and Galileo and others who supported the Copernican theory were only pardoned by the Church after more than 300 years for their heresy in 1969. Philosophers and experimentalists gradually probed natural phenomena and the concept of a scientific method was established and gained support in Western countries. Although there are a variety of approaches to the scientific method, the essential idea is that to explain a phenomenon which arouses curiosity and conflict an hypothesis is stated and then experiments are devised to test the hypothesis. If all the experiments support the idea it becomes part of the canon of knowledge but failure results in its rejection. There are many hazards to this approach involving genuine mistakes in interpreting experimental results. The progress of science spawned by the experimental method is reinforced by the fact that it works even if the ideas are counter-intuitive. So the faith we have in the likelihood of a successful journey by air depends on multiple trial and error experiments on theories of flight, power and reliability of

School and the Massachusetts General Hospital. On October 13th 2013 the journal Nature exposed the fraudulent claims when it checked with Harvard Medical School and the Massachusetts General Hospital, neither of which institutions had any affiliation with Moriguchi who publically admitted the fraud.

These are just prominent examples of fraud in science where claims have been made that could if true have been major contributions to advance science but in fact had the opposite effect and highlighted the disreputable practices of some scientists. There have been worries expressed by the editors of all the leading scientific journals, not only concerning specific cases that have come to light, but also anxious that fraud in science is probably quite common, though usually at much lower level than the above examples and since most are not investigated publically the extent is unknown.

However if something works it will become accepted and may be for the good of humanity and the planet but sadly the reverse is also true. As has been the theme of this book, once established by a reliable scientific method, knowledge cannot be unlearned. The cat is out of the bag although curiosity may kill the cat.

THE PLASTICITY OF THE BRAIN

Large animals have large brains but the ratio of the size of the brain to that of the animals is important. The crow and parrot birds have exceptionally large brains for their body size and the New Caledonian Crows construct beautiful tools for hunting. They teach their skills to their young so biologists studying these birds describe their acquired practical knowledge as "a ratchet" in the same sense as that used in this book.

In the course of foetal development the cells destined to become brain cells migrate to the preordained part of the developing embryo and become organised in an immensely complicated way so that they engines, properties of strength and weight of materials used in construction, and now extremely accurate determination of the exact whereabouts of the plane, its speed, height and progress in its journey. The satellite navigation that is ubiquitous depends on quantum concepts of sub-atomic physics which are certainly counter-intuitive to most non-experts. The fact that light can at the same time be particulate and also a wave form of energy is not easy to understand, especially when trying to measure the wave and particulate aspects of light alters their properties. No doubt the evolution of the brain was not subjected to mathematic concepts of subatomic physics. Nevertheless the nature of subatomic physics has been verified in numerous ways and clearly works and is responsible for an integral part of the electronic digital internet "miracle" with which we are familiar and regard as essential.

Whenever the cutting edge of science is probed, the enormity of our ignorance is exposed. In his book entitled "Ignorance" Professor Stuart Firestein referred to advances in science as difficult to achieve, rather like searching for 'a black cat in a dark room' and since our ignorance is so great we do not know for sure that there is a cat in the room. Of course the eyesight of cats in the dark is excellent and may result in serendipity with the cat jumping into our arms for a bit of comfort and love and telling us the secret we are seeking.

Progress in science has always been a perilous journey, like walking on stepping-stones in a marsh, it is easy to stumble on a stone one did not know was there or put one's foot in the marsh where it was thought there was a stone. Nevertheless the rewards in science can be huge so that humans will be tempted to adopt short cuts to personal advantage in fame and riches. The mass of scientific literature is increasing in an exponential manner, not only because of the increased activity, but also due to a proliferation of new journals, so that eventually almost any manuscript will be accepted. Demanding recognition in citations by other scientists is interpreted as a positive achievement and a goal for some members of the scientific community almost irrespective of the quality of the work.

There are four categories of scientific paper although they are not completely separate and clear cut.

1. A paper describing a new and important observation or concept that can be repeated in independent laboratories and has ramifications that will constitute a leap in knowledge and potential application.
2. A paper describing a phenomenon that is of little interest to most scientists where the work has nevertheless been conducted and interpreted correctly. Such a communication will be read by few.
3. A study that claims to have made a leap forward, but cannot be replicated in an independent laboratory and is eventually shown to be a result of poorly conducted experiments or misinterpretation of data. The humiliation of failing is difficult to accept and the mistakes of work in Category 3 may not be admitted, shifting it to Category 4.
4. A scientific publication that is deliberately fraudulent where the authors have set out to confuse fellow scientists with spurious data for the purpose of personal advancement, increase in salary and fame.

If this last category challenges important concepts, failure to reproduce the experimental data in another laboratory will eventually expose the fraud. In fact the greater the fraudulent claim the more likely the misbehaviour will be exposed. Nevertheless, fraud is common as is misinterpretation of data, so one has to be very cautious in accepting new claims. The media latch on to so-called scientific discoveries before they have been confirmed, especially in matters relating to health, so there is a continuous stream of misinformation given to the public with totally spurious warnings and advice to avoid or partake excessively in eating certain foods or indulging in special activities. The media seem to thrive on th expectation that if you know nothing you will believe anything. 1 one listened to all the health warnings and exhortation: sympathetically one's sanity would be severely challenged.

All science is prey to fraudulent practices but biological sciences are especially vulnerable. In 2010 The Lancet retracted a paper that had caused alarm to the general public concerning the safety of the measles, mumps and rubella (MMR) vaccine. Andrew Wakefield had claimed that the vaccine was a cause of autism in children. These conclusions were based on incorrect data, the result of unsatisfactory trials and misrepresentation of the findings. It led to a wave of fear and refusal of parents to have their children vaccinated, leaving many unprotected.

In 1974 a dramatic claim by William Summerlin at the famous Sloan-Kettering Institute in New York, reported that culture of skin in the laboratory prior to transplantation avoided rejection. His results presented at an international meeting in San Francisco seemed to me to be too good to be true and so I was not surprised when the fraud was discovered, albeit in a rather prosaic circumstance. The perpetrator was observed painting the skin grafts with a felt pen in the Institution's elevator to pretend they were not rejected.

The Italian doctor, Zamboni, caused widespread excitement when he claimed that defects of venous drainage of the brain were responsible for multiple sclerosis. Hopes were raised for many patients only for them to be dashed when the data were shown to be flawed with no supporting evidence in independent trials.

Recently there was a really bizarre fraud in stem cell research by Hisashi Moriguchi from Tokyo University, who claimed that he had used iPS cells of liver origin to treat successfully heart failure patients. This achievement from the University of Tokyo had worldwide publicity when it was reported in the "Yomiuri Shimbun" newspaper which has the largest circulation of any newspaper in the world. Moriguchi said he had an affiliation to Harvard Medical can connect with each other and control the sensations, movement, memory and thought in the brain. Some specialised cell clusters have separate names, for example amigdella/emotions, hippocampus/ memory, olfactory bulb/smell. Progenitor cells are widely distributed in the embryo and can differentiate into motor, sensory or other specialized neurons. The plasticity of these cells in neonatal and early life is remarkable. A child suffering from potentially lethal *status epilepticus* may be treated as a last resort by removing one whole cerebral hemisphere, yet recovery can be rapid and nearly complete if the surgery is performed at a very early age with only moderate brain damage demonstrable on examination of the patient after the operation. In an adult such an operation would lead to permanent severe disability with hemiplegia and gross neurological disturbances. Nevertheless even in the adult there are possibilities of repair after damage. A celebrated case of an American railroad worker, Phineas Gage was well recorded. He was using dynamite to remove a rock and there was a premature explosion which drove an iron bar through his head as shown in the illustration of his skull (Figure 16a). Yet to the amazement of those who witnessed the accident, after only a short period of unconsciousness, Mr. Gage woke up and started to move and recovered sufficiently well to return to work, where he was photographed as shown in Figure 16b holding the iron bar that went through his skull.

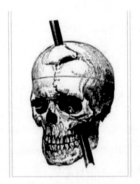

Figure 16a. Iron bar driven through the skull of Phineas Gage in a dynamite accident.

Figure 16b. Photograph of Pineas Gage holding the bar, having made a remarkable recovery.

In the middle of the last century many operations were performed involving cutting the connections between the frontal lobes and the rest of the brain, usually to treat obsessional disorders. Patients following this operation were often observed to have changed personalities and depending on the severity of the cut, incidents and situations that previously would have been very distressing no longer bothered them. Phineas Gage's colleagues noticed that his personality changed after the accident despite his remarkable recovery. They said he was he was no longer "Gage".

Repetitive and intense psychological pressure is very successful in the manipulation of the thoughts and actions of young children. This has been and continues to be practised in certain orthodox religious institutions and also in quasi-religious sects which have espoused terrorism, as in the Sarin gas underground attach in Tokyo. This effective brainwashing or "holy waterboarding" has been a central feature of the propaganda of all dictatorships and is also used in democratic Western countries to persuade people to adopt the wishes of the Government, for instance to stop smoking but has been less effective in curing those who are addicted to hard drugs.

In the adult brain there are a few areas that contain progenitor cells capable of differentiating into a variety of cell types, some are found in the adult nasal apparatus, the olfactory bulb and in the hippocampus. In Cambridge interesting recent experiments were reported in Dachshund dogs partially paralysed by damage to their spinal cords, a natural hazard of the German Sausage dog. Nerve sheath cells taken from the nasal sinus were transplanted to the same dog, above, into and below the damaged spinal cord. This resulted in recovery of movement of the previously paralysed lower limbs. Interestingly the co-ordination of movements became linked to the movement of the upper limbs but did not extend to the brain. Videos show the dogs with lower limb paralysis able to run again after autotransplantation of their own nasal nerve sheath cells. (Granger, N., Blamires, H. et al., *Brain* 135: 3227-3237, 2012).

We are at an early stage of understanding the physiology of the brain, but imaging techniques have moved very quickly and it is now possible to determine by functional magnetic resonance studies which parts of the brain are active at a given time by the amount of blood flowing to them. There can be no doubt that attempts will be made to utilise these techniques to treat disorders of the brain and spinal cord by means of drugs and surgery. Already it is possible to pinpoint the site in the brain for the delivery of a drug or cells to be transplanted using imaging techniques and these will soon become refined and presumably managed robotically. The techniques and drugs developed for the treatment of brain disease and damage will probably be seized upon by unscrupulous people and nations to manipulate brain activities of adversaries, possibly by the use of a chemical distributed in the air or in water.

Recent experiments in mice with electrodes inserted into the hippocampal region of the brain showed that stimulation of the nerve cells could introduce false memories, a very worrying development in neurological science as a possible means of control (Ramirez, S. et al., *Science* 341, 387-391, 2013).

There is a tendency to violence and conflict in the human psyche, as witnessed by the mayhem that follows removal of a police force even in what are regarded as highly civilised communities. Science will help to clarify brain function and how disease and disturbance occur and point to methods of treatment that may alleviate disorder and the dangers of a malfunctioning brain, but could also be used for enforcement of dictatorial policies.

BRAVE NEW WORLD; 1984 HUXLEY AND ORWELL; SURVEILLANCE AND CONTROL OF INDIVIDUALS BY THE STATE

The novels of Aldous Huxley and George Orwell seemed bizarre and quite unreal at the time when they were written, although some people found them very disquieting. Unfortunately now much has come to pass as they predicted. We have surrendered an enormous amount of our identity voluntarily to the internet, the so-called 'cloud' back-up services, which were designed to appear seducingly comforting, in fact provide Google, Facebook and Twitter with our intimate details *gratis* without protest. The state now has authority for the Police and other security agencies to record and have access in perpetuity to our personal conversations and messages stored in the "clouds" of internet companies. In the course of a number of years almost every individual will have delivered opinions and statements that later they would regret and perhaps were only recorded in a moment of anger, envy or frustration. Yet these details could be used selectively and out of context to implicate each of us as damning evidence against us and confronting us with our sins of a lifetime previously a prerogative of the Almighty on the Day of Judgement (Figure 17).

Figure 17. The seductive cloud holding all your secrets available to the Government.
Cloud painting by John Constable.

THE HUMAN GENOME

"We are lucky dips in a bag of chips off the block of the Family Tree."

(Dr. Patrick Montgomery, Guys' Residents Play 1953)

The whole human genome can be typed currently for about $1000 and pertinent sections of it for $100 and the cost rapidly continues to fall. This information is a potential cause of great social upheaval and distress. We know certain genes of rare and fatal diseases such as haemophilia, cystic fibrosis and Huntington's chorea are inherited and details of the inheritance can influence individuals as to whether to have children. More subtle tendencies to illness are already beginning to be recognized in portions of the genome, for instance the susceptibility to develop breast, colon or prostatic cancer, the development of rheumatoid or osteo-arthritis and perhaps early age onset of dementia, multiple sclerosis, schizophrenia and bi-polar disease. Sooner or later Insurance companies will require this genetic information before issuing a policy. These are just examples of risk factors which can be assessed numerically by actuarial means and could be a major influence in choosing a spouse. Beautiful or handsome youngsters will certainly lose their looks as they get older, but it is becoming increasingly possible to assess not only their likelihood of becoming diseased but also the potential of disease affecting children of the marriage or partnership. The celebrity phenotype of a beautiful young couple may have a sinister genomic sword of Damocles hanging over their future to be revealed and wrestled with when the two genomes are analysed.

Marriage in one form or another has been a feature of all main civilisations and has persisted as an aim in most Western countries. The stability and happiness of the family derived from the institution of marriage has been remarkably successful in all enduring cultures. Historically in many cultures the marriage arrangements have been entrusted to a matchmaker chosen for experience, wisdom and an understanding of the culture, religion and objectives of the marriage union. Science has now provided the modern equivalent of a marriage matchmaker with a whole new book of data concerning the humans genome with all the ramifications, many of which are currently uncertain (Figure 18). Each refinement in genetics will provide reasonable odds for a couple being unsuitable in terms of genes that might combine to produce seriously diseased offspring or the likelihood of one or other of the couple developing an illness such as dementia or arthritis at an early age. No doubt these factors will play an increasing part in marriage arrangements and marriage itself has been criticised and disparaged in many liberal Western communities. But however convenient this might be for the partners concerned, there are worrying *sequelae* to a satisfactory upbringing of children.

Figure 18. Chinese matchmaker planning a wedding. The modern matchmaker will have new and vital information to include the genomes of the bride and groom.

SOCIETY AND SOCIAL MEDIA

The astounding success of the internet applications of social media, in particular Facebook and Twitter, was a surprise to those who invented these social media and coincided with the extraordinary popularity of internet games, often extremely violent, which are enjoyed by nearly all youngsters, even those who have not yet reached their teenage years. Their enjoyment is frequently so intense that it becomes an obsession and absorbs many hours of the day and night in an unproductive consumption of time. Many adults also have a similar love of blogging using Facebook and commenting on Twitter. All this passion on internet social communication seems strange, one wonders how the needs which they fulfil were consummated before the internet. Chat, community gatherings, religion and for children especially, outdoor games may have been the alternatives. Sports, often of a competitive nature are now forbidden in many countries by so-called "health and safety laws", which cripple the ability of the child to face the world. Incessant, passive enjoyment of popular music is also apparently a joyful pursuit, or at least an activity that is almost essential for many people, young and old. More and more people in trains, restaurants, walking in the street, cycling and jogging have wires dangling from their ears or are immersed in mobile Smart phones. In restaurants it is not uncommon for couples to be seen spending most of the evening talking on the phone to third persons and paying no attention to each other. Of course new crazes in fashions are always criticised by older people who remember what they considered were better times, but the changes have already been wrought in society. They have been very significant and seem to have no signs of slowing down. The internet has many innovative ramifications and has much to answer for, not always beneficial.

Science has influenced the practice of sexual activity. The likelihood of pregnancy was a restraining factor in casual sexual intercourse until there were improvements in the manufacture of condoms and the contraceptive pill. With both mechanical and pharmacological prevention of pregnancy available, attitudes to what would previously have been serious risk-taking have changed. Also sexual activity, certainly in men, has had a renaissance with the introduction of pharmacological prevention of impotence so that inadequacy of sexual performance can in many cases be treated successfully. *In vitro* fertilisation has permitted millions of previously infertile couples to have children.

Many youngsters even in their early teens at school experiment with sex and this is often no longer regarded by authorities as a practice to be condemned. Although the law in the UK specifies that sex below 16 is a crime, it is a crime that seems never to have been taken seriously when both participants are below 16, yet conception is perfectly possible in young teenagers at a time when the frontal lobes of the brains of the juvenile parents have not fully developed and the responsibilities of bringing a child into the world are not understood, nor the sacrifices that will be necessary if their children are going to have a fair start in the life.

The ideas of Francis Galton, which were seized upon as a eugenic scientific backing for racists and political persecution by the Nazis, was justifiably discredited, but now there is increasing scientific information of the potential of the genes we carry and mutations that have already occurred or are likely in the future. All these unwelcome thoughts are the result of application of science which in many cases began just as curiosity. When Crick and Watson were in the Eagle pub in Cambridge, having worked out the basic structure of DNA and proclaimed to those who happened to be in the pub that they, Crick and Watson, had discovered the "secret of life" and were therefore offering everyone a free drink, they must have had little in their minds apart from euphoria and certainly not the more sombre sequelae that I have outlined above.

The internet, with digitisation of information, stores and retains with great accuracy all the details that we surrender voluntarily, for example face recognition. The installation of CCTV cameras in all city centres, many offices and private residences may provide security from violence and lead to apprehension of criminals, as can minute traces of DNA, which with an uncanny accuracy can help identify the individual who left the trace. The recognition on CCTV cameras of the Boston Marathon bombers led to their rapid discovery and these techniques will become even more widespread and accurate as technology continues its unstoppable advances. It is doubtful that the poor individual who has committed no crime will be able to have a defence against this invasion of privacy. We have rolled on our backs with our legs in the air to embrace these advances which may well be used to crush us. Huxley and Orwell have been well justified in their warnings of things to come.

The electronic credit card has revolutionised financial transactions, facilitating the buying, selling and payment of nearly all aspects of purchase and personal banking. It has, however, had weaknesses which have been exploited on a large scale. It is an important component of electronic surveillance discussed in this chapter, since every transaction is recorded, not only the date and time but also where and to whom the payments were made. It is also a very attractive target for criminals who steal cards or copy and clone them surreptitiously to defraud the customer and the bank. Despite all the safeguards introduced and updated, credit card fraud rob banks regularly of large sums on a major scale that seems to be very difficult to control. Profiling of customers' data by the credit card companies is used by advertising agencies to select targets according to the details from the credit card transaction.

Criminals on remand are often required to wear a tag so that their movements can be recorded, but many free citizens will pay for their own tag and give the same continuous information of their whereabouts by their mobile phone, which can be tracked by the phone company and pinpointed using satellite navigation. So surveillance of the individual is now almost complete.

The next step in science fiction would be to read the mind by imaging procedures yet to be developed. How the state and other authorities will handle the clutter of information that is available to them depends on the structure of society and government, but sadly there is a tendency, even in democracies, that the availability of powers, primarily conceived for the good of society, will nevertheless be abused to the detriment of the individual's freedom. The Smart phones have influenced peoples' behaviour, especially children; social intercourse has changed and there is far less face-to-face conversation. For all its manifest convenience and apparent advantages the Smart phone may be a poisoned chalice. This appeared to be the assessment of Angela Merkl and Francois Hollande, heads of State whose Smart phones have been systematically hacked into for years by the US secret surveillance institutions. The demonstration of lack of faith between allies interferes with previous friendly international relations.

Cyber bullying is a very serious antisocial and dangerous activity, especially involving children but adults are also vulnerable. The temptation to reveal personal details and inappropriate images especially of a sexual nature renders the individual a target for blackmail. In schools from widely different communities this practice of "sexting" is widespread and driven by peer pressure. There are a number of laws involving cyber bullying which may be classified as a crime but there are many alternative avenues in the internet for vulnerable people to expose themselves and become not only humiliated but also to be driven to self concepts of worthlessness that may lead to suicide. How this can be handled is very difficult but compassionate education and availability of helplines to which the vulnerable can turn are now being offered and may give useful lifesaving guidance.

SOME CIVILIAN CONSEQUENCES OF SCIENCE

The digital era with the development of the internet and increasingly complicated tasks being accomplished by clever new robots, is changing our way of life. Robotic machines are taking over all manufacturing processes. Robotic management of car driving will hopefully increase the safety and reduce the hassle of driving and robots would be forbidden to develop "road rage". They will become more prominent in household chores, such as cleaning, washing dishes, washing clothes and already there has been a major swing towards online shopping, including banking. All these apparently good things have downsides. Digital photography eventually made 140,000 people unemployed when the huge Kodak Company folded. There is almost a daily list of important shops, particularly shopping franchises, becoming insolvent, as consumers turn towards online shopping with avoidance of a trip to the main street. However, online shopping has disadvantages. To see the goods on offer, to meet friends and to socialise as part of the shopping experience and enjoyment is lost with online ordering.

Internet communication allows advertising, the propagation of state policy and control over the individual to become an intrusive "reach out". It is extraordinary how widespread is the love of the mobile phone or tablet, especially amongst the young beginning to supersede the craving to watch television. Instead of eye contact, facial and hand expression fulfilling social intercourse, people bend their heads and dextrously flip the controls of their digital machine and many children become obsessed with games which they play with themselves and their contacts. Often the games involve extreme violence and easy access to pornography, which is usually portrayed in an unreal manner without the joy and intimacy that should be encountered between the sexes. None of the activities alluded to above can be stopped and instead they will increase. New technologies will be invented, utilising scientific advances and illustrating the ratchet properties that can not be unlearned. Increase in unemployment, much of it a consequence of application of science, is very serious especially for young and dissatisfied people who cannot get worthwhile jobs and may take their grievances to the streets with conflict that cannot be easily contained.

THE FRIENDLY ATOM

During the 1890s x-rays were discovered by Rontgen, radioactivity as a spontaneous emission from Uranium by Becquerel and radium and its irradiation properties by Marie and Pierre Curie. These temporal concentrations of fundamental physics discoveries were investigated in many different laboratories but harmful effects were slow to be recognised. Translation of the properties of irradiation were used in medicine and industry in the subsequent 100 years. As with so many important discoveries, there were many players in the team but Wilhelm Rontgen, Professor of physics in Wurzburg, was the first to discover and suggest the possibility of using electromagnetic radiation to image internal anatomy in medicine and famously in 1896 x-rayed his wife's hand. (Figure 19). Rontgen, Becquerel and Marie and Pierre Curie all received Nobel Prizes. The Curies' purification of the element radium provided a tool for treatment of some cancers by damaging the structure of DNA in rapidly dividing malignant cells. A similar biological effect resulted from electromagnetic ionising x-ray irradiation. This consisted of a stream of electrons emitted from a cathode ray tube subjected to high voltage electricity, whereas atomic radiation came spontaneously from heavy radioactive elements.

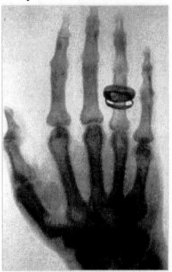

An X-ray picture (radiograph), taken by Wilhelm Röntgen, of his wife's hand.

Figure 19. The first x-ray taken by Wilheim Röntgen of his wife's hand.

The ramifications of this early application and development of these groundbreaking discoveries have been enormous. The energy of disintegrating atoms has been harnessed for both weapons and peaceful uses. In medicine x-rays allowed vision of anatomy inside the living body, particularly bones and then later computerised tomographic multiple x-ray (CT) scanning provided excellent imaging of soft structures within the body and completely transformed medicine by enabling accurate diagnosis in areas that previously had to be assessed by clinical examination and direct surgical inspection. Magnetic resonance (MR) scanning soon followed CT scanning giving additional and alternative information without subjecting the patient to x-irradiation. Radio-isotope labelled atoms led to important discoveries in physiology and metabolism and are also used in determining the nature and situation of pathological processes and in hospital laboratories for biochemical analyses and treatments.

The destructive effects of irradiation are applied to sterilise materials, especially surgical instruments without having to use heat and also to treat animals, particularly insects which can be rendered sterile and then introduced into the wild where they can undermine the normal fertility of the species, so that the pests are no longer available in the areas where they damage crops or spread diseases.

Shortly after the atom bombs were dropped in Japan, physicists devised a method of slowing down the thermonuclear reaction in a controlled manner so that the disintegration of uranium from neutron bombardment resulted in release of heat to produce steam that is harnessed directly in mechanical power and electricity generation. There are however caveats in the use of nuclear energy in this manner. It certainly works in static power plants and has been very successful in driving large ships and especially submarines. The advantage in the submarine is the absence of noxious gases. The atomic motor causes little noise and allows submarines to remain underwater for very long periods. This must be stressful for the crews, particularly since submarines carrying atomic warhead Polaris missiles are sometimes submerged for weeks or even months at a time. A small amount of nuclear material can provide energy millions of times greater than that produced by coal and oil. The fuel used in submarines requires more highly enriched uranium 235 than that used in atomic power plants.

The use of nuclear power releases little pollution into the atmosphere and currently is responsible for 17% of the world's energy. However all nuclear energy installations are subject to potential danger of so-called "melt down", with an explosive release of radioactive elements into the atmosphere, water supply and the soil. There were disastrous consequences of the Chernobyl reactors melt-down. Recently the Fukushima power station sustained simultaneously the double blow from a massive earthquake, which cut off much of the fail-safe installations, and immediately after this was followed by a huge tsunami which caused devastating explosions from the plant and scatter of irradiation over miles in the air, in the sea and soil. The full scale of the disaster is not yet known and harm continues as the dangerous material is still escaping. There have also been disasters in nuclear-powered ships with similar release of radioactive material but on a much smaller scale.

With all atomic powered installations throughout the world there comes a time when something has to be done with the residual spent fuel which is still radioactive. Some can be recycled but a radioactive residue remains which has proved to be very difficult to manage. Nobody wants it buried on or near their land and some of the radioactivity may last for many, even thousands of years. There have been intense, heated and sometimes out of control debates between those in favour of the use of nuclear energy and those against. The more violent the confrontation between the two sides the less can be achieved in fully understanding what is involved and the best action to take.

The demand for energy is increasing worldwide and will continue to do so. The harm produced by the consumption of fossil fuels is obvious enough even if its influence on climate change can be debated, but on air pollution there can be no argument and efforts to reduce the release of toxic materials from the burning of coal, oil, and gas have been only partially successful. Renewable energy from crops, plants, the wind, tides and the sun are all becoming alternatives to fossil fuels, but renewable sources of energy are expensive and the amount of energy produced does not yet, and seems unlikely in the future to address the demand. Most of the natural sources of energy for example hydroelectric electricity generation have now been capitalised and construction of new dams will damage the environment and cause distress to both humans and wild life inundated by the rise in water level above the dams. Energy can also be captured from natural hot springs which points to the vast source of heat which might one day be tapped below the surface of the earth.

Much effort has been expended on trying to make atomic energy safer and more efficient. A breeder reactor in nuclear power can produce more fissile material than it uses, from both uranium 238 and plutonium. Sadly after more than 60 years the hopes of breeder reactors have not been fulfilled. Another approach on which there were great expectations is to utilise fusion of different atomic particles together with the release of vast amounts of neutrons to provide energy. This is a much cleaner process than fission. To produce a commercial fusion reactor has so far eluded the designers and the amount of energy produced has been less than the energy required from electricity to set up the reactor. Nevertheless theoretically fusion is attractive, avoiding much of the side effects of fission. The energy of the sun from which we derive our life-giving environment comes from fusion of hydrogen to form the heavier molecule helium. Evolution of the stars involves nuclear synthesis with fusion of small elements into larger ones, which then fuse further when the star eventually explodes, releasing a variety of elements into stella space. This theory of the English astrophysicist Fred Hoyle in 1954 was a solution to the previous ignorance of how the elements were formed. The sun is the ultimate and literal "global" energy plant and perhaps we will be able in the future to derive more benefit from this ubiquitous source.

Chapter V

MEDICAL SCIENCE

Medicine had no scientific background until the circulation of the blood was discovered by William Harvey in the early 17th Century, putting together recent anatomical studies with his own experiments. Harvey demonstrated circulation of blood in arteries and veins through the heart and lungs that could only make sense if there were minute capillary connections in the tissues between the arterial and venous systems. So his revolutionary proposal depended on the existence of vessels too small to see, but as he reasoned, had to be there. Initially he was cautious in presenting his ideas for fear of the heavy hand of authority and particularly the Church, censoring him and possibly inflicting punishment. But the circulation of the blood was the foundation of our understanding of mammalian physiology and the development of the microscope revealed that Harvey was absolutely right and moreover, soon showed the cellular basis of living matter and the ubiquitous existence of minute organisms, too small to be seen with the naked eye, some of which were causally associated with severe diseases. A visit to the doctor before these discoveries was likely to do more harm than good. For hundreds of years the majority of illnesses were treated with bloodletting, which made the patients sicker and hastened their demise. The surgical management of wounds could save lives, but amputation of damaged or gangrenous limbs was often complicated by lethal infection and a terrifying high mortality rate that occurred, even with the simplest of surgical procedures. Lister in the United Kingdom and Semmelweis in Austria recognised that the source of contagion was introduced at the time of the operation or during birth, the culprit frequently being the doctor, whose hands were contaminated. Antiseptic and later aseptic surgery revolutionised surgical care and made surgery an acceptable treatment even for elective procedures.

Traditional medicines had been used in Europe, China and India for thousands of years and many folk medicines are still not fully understood as to which are active, which have no effect and which are positively dangerous. However morphine has stood the test of time and also digitalis extracted from the foxglove by William Withering in the 18th Century is still used in heart failure. At the end of the 18th Century Jenner introduced vaccination with cowpox, which produced a mild skin eruption and gave protection from the dangerous related disease Smallpox. Pasteur greatly reduced the danger of tuberculosis by heating or "pasteurising" milk which killed the tubercle bacilli. He also introduced a vaccine against rabies which, if administered soon enough after a dog bite from a rabid animal, could prevent death from this previously universally fatal disease.

Concerted effort by scientists throughout the world produced powerful vaccines that have eliminated the scourge of smallpox and poliomyelitis is confined to a few areas. Sadly attempts to vaccinate children at risk in Pakistan and Nigeria have met with violent opposition and savage murder of nurses who have devoted their lives to trying to protect children from this horrible, paralytic disease.

Improvement in general hygiene, the establishment of nursing as a noble profession, championed by Florence Nightingale and especially the supply of clean water were important advances in preventing communicable diseases due to infection. The discovery of antibacterial drugs, the sulphomamides, in Germany in the 1930s by the dye chemist, Gerhard Domagk working in the Bayer Company, and penicillin by Fleming, Chain and Florey in the 1940s in England were the start of a very successful onslaught on micro-organisms. Fleming's observation of the bacterial killing effect of the fungal mould *Penicillium notatum* led to a search for and discovery of powerful medicines in natural products. Unfortunately many pathogenic bacteria and viruses develop resistance to antibiotics and some pathogenic species are now extremely difficult to treat, especially the *methicillin-resistant Staphylococcus aureus* (MRSA) and *Clostridium difficile* (CD). Tuberculosis has also re-emerged with a resistant bacillus that spreads rapidly and is proving very difficult to control.

The introduction of safe anaesthetics at the end of the 19th century transformed surgery from a brutal pursuit to a civilised curative treatment. The conquest of many diseases has been remarkable and has reduced infant mortality and the death rate in young children which were once extremely common. Historical records of the 19th Century and the tragedies portrayed in Victorian novels are testimony to the frequency of the deaths of young children and also of women in childbirth. Advances in medicine have been the consequence of evidence-based science and have changed the pattern of disease throughout the world. The extreme increase in the world population in the past 50 years, which still continues, is putting a strain on resources of food and water and has increased contamination of the air, which is probably a major component of observed global warming. In China and India the preponderance of boys has been deliberately skewed by abortions and infanticide of female foetuses and babies. It seems that in communities where women receive good education, the number of desired children is reduced and in fact, childbirth is often delayed until women have finished their education and established themselves in work. This, together with contraception, may slow down the population growth. Improved medical care is also responsible for the increasing lifespan observed worldwide, many people surviving into their eighties and nineties, but sadly chronic illnesses are companions of old age, diminishing the quality of life with reduction in mobility and rising numbers of sufferers from dementia. The costs of the care of the aged, who cannot look after themselves, is increasing and caring for the aged requires dedication and compassion, often devolved to low paid workers not always selected for their humanity.

Advances in medical sciences have certainly improved the quality of life of millions of people, but the consequences as outlined above are important and need serious consideration as to how they can be managed. The demographics of the sex ratio in India and China clearly show the artificial skewed preponderance of boys, the so-called "missing girls" can and have led to social problems which are difficult to resolve. Ultrasound scanning of the pregnant uterus can determine the sex of the embryo and may influence parents to demand an abortion. Sadly murder of female babies is common when early abortion has not been available. Despite all the benefits that have accrued it would not be unreasonable to blame the over-population and the human contribution to climate warming at least in part to advances in medical science.

The actual techniques of surgical operations have changed and are continuing to change at a rapid rate and very minute powerful telescopes have been fashioned which can be introduced through small, almost buttonhole, incisions into various parts of the body. These telescopes and the instruments that work with them are now being manipulated partially by robotic machines which eliminate any shaking in the surgeons' hands and also provide excellent vision of the parts to be operated on and how to proceed with the operation. If however there is an unexpected error, for example a sudden bleed, surgeons trained in endoscopic surgery are often ill-prepared to deal with the emergency that requires swift conventional operating techniques if there is to be a chance of saving the patients.

New drugs have been produced to kill bacteria and viruses and also to treat cancer. Some of these drugs are extremely expensive and in exceptional cases one patient may need between 50,000 and 100,000 dollars-worth of drugs a year to control a malignant growth. Cancer is now considered to be a genetic disease, not only the susceptibility to develop cancer, but also gene changes in the malignant cells that mutate making them resistant to first order anticancer drugs. So new treatment strategies follow the successful pattern now used in the treatment of HIV/AIDS to start treatment with a cocktail of drugs in the hope of a pre-emptive strike before the emergence of mutated resistant malignant cells. The genome of the cancer compared to that of the patient will in future direct the oncologist towards the most effective drug cocktail. New antibiotics designed to overcome the resistance to the old ones are also very expensive. So it is now becoming difficult for those planning healthcare to provide everyone in need with the best treatment available. Health costs are escalating as the techniques improve and expensive imaging allows doctors to obtain a good view of all parts of the body, so that early anatomical diagnosis is accurately pinpointed by non-invasive means and patients are demanding the most up to date and usually the most expensive treatment. Even the richest nations will have to introduce some form of "rationing" as medical expenses exceed the realistic capabilities of every country.

Transplantation of vital organs has now passed through the phase of scepticism into general acceptance but genetic engineering and stem cell treatment have received media hype far in excess of the state of the art. The building blocks are known but there would appear to be important missing pieces of the puzzle that remain to be discovered. By analogy blood transfusion was attempted, both experimentally and therapeutically, in the 17th century. The polymath architect Christopher Wren was one of a group of enthusiastic experimenters who showed that the procedure of blood transfusion could be done using a sharpened feather quill, a precursor of the hypodermic needle. But at that time there was no concept of blood groups nor was there any way of preventing blood from clotting, so the results were disastrous and when attempted in patients usually fatal. It required these previously unknown factors to be clarified before blood transfusion could be done safely. This was an important lesson that needs to be learned; the mere performance of an operation does not ensure success if there is ignorance of vital relevant physiological information.

In what is now called "regenerative medicine" there have been significant advances in understanding how tissues are differentiated in the embryo, the role of genes producing specific proteins and micro-manipulation of cells to change their genomic and phenotypic characteristics would seem to justify cautious optimism that therapeutic applications will be found. No doubt stumbling blocks will also be encountered.

It can be useful to be aware of one's ignorance, for example consider the following in three species, the dog, the newt and the Zebra fish; the dog and man have been together for ten thousand years but the dog's lifespan is usually between 15 and 16 years. The life span of humans until recently was around 60 years with exceptions reaching beyond 100. Longevity has certainly increased, but apart from certain biblical characters, to live beyond 100 is unusual. But why is the dog's life span so much less than humans? The dog cares for its young for a much shorter period and the young become independent and in the wild hunt in packs after about 6 months, but then after 15 years ageing sets in and this process is not understood. It seems to be biologically programmed.

The newt is a primitive amphibian that has highly advanced regenerative properties, so that if it loses a tail or a limb, replacements grow rapidly with remarkable accuracy. After amputation, a small number of residual stem cells cooperate to produce bone, muscle, nerves, blood vessel and skin, with joints to allow appropriate articulation in the limbs. Unfortunately there is no evidence in man that such cells with these extraordinary properties exist or could be organised as in the newt. Cell differentiation to produce the separate organs occurs in the foetus of all species, but we do not know if a similar process might be possible to engineer in an adult human.

The Zebra fish is very popular in biological studies because it is small, translucent and easy to keep in the laboratory and its heart has remarkable powers of regeneration after it has been damaged. We know that stem cells are present in all tissues in the body including the heart and presumably these cells participate in the repair of the Zebra fishes' damaged hearts, but again this does not mean that the stem cells in human hearts would have the same capabilities. For scientists to work towards this end makes sense and is reasonable, but early success cannot be assumed. There are many other examples of our ignorance but the limitations of what we know and can do is no deterrent to quack doctors to offer so called "stem cell and gene therapy" to desperate patients, who will try anything if they can be persuaded there is even a small chance of success. These criminal doctors manipulate the fears of vulnerable patients to extract high fees.

The causes of most diseases and their mode of spread were quite unknown until the existence of bacteria was visualised in the late 18th century. The next step was to recognise that certain bacteria were responsible for common scourges, for example, tuberculosis, cholera and plague. Blood-borne parasites were shown to cause malaria. Very much smaller organisms called viruses were later identified as the cause of influenza, yellow fever, measles, rabies, chickenpox, smallpox and more recently several forms of hepatitis and HIV/AIDS. Spread of infectious diseases is sometimes by direct contact, in other cases there are insect vectors such as mosquitoes, flies, and fleas. In plague, in addition to fleas, there is an intermediate host – the rat. An understanding of the rat-flea-human spread of plague came to a young French Doctor, Paul-Louis Simond, in the 1890s who, in a plague outbreak in India, listened to villagers who told him rats came out of the sewers, coughing blood and then died; 3-4 days later humans are struck down by Bubonic Plague. Dr. Simond suspected rat fleas were leaving the cold bodies of the dead rats and moving to the warmth of humans. At enormous personal risk he dissected affected rats and found the plague bacillus. His observations were treated with extreme scepticism by the medical hierarchy. They were later accepted and publicised by others who carelessly forgot the original brilliant work of Simond who was relegated to obscurity. Life is often unfair, especially in attributing credit correctly.

Now we have unravelled the often far-from obvious trails of infection. We have developed antibiotics that will control or cure many ailments. The other mode of prevention and control of disease is to harness and enhance the body's natural tendency to battle infection by immunising with vaccines, so that antibodies and protective cells are primed and ready to eliminate infecting organisms.

These few examples of important medical advances are the flowering of the scientific "seeds" identified and planted as a result of our understanding of anatomy and physiology. Hygienic concepts, antiseptic and later aseptic surgery coupled with the provision of clean drinking water, uncontaminated by sewage were important advances in reducing morbidity, mortality and misery.

"Evidence based medicine" demonstrated the harm caused by smoking, alcohol, radioactive materials and asbestos, but *pari passu* with these well-researched causative associations with disease. There has been a plethora of pseudoscientific claims pounced on with delight and usually distorted by the media. Breast feeding, red wine, aspirin, statins, have each been hailed as almost miraculous causes of good health and longevity one day, and the devil's strategies for harm the next. The only defence from such confusing declamations is to stop reading newspapers, listening to radio and most difficult of all, watching television. The advice of St Benedict is wise "*all things in moderation*" including "*drinking no more than one hemina (one pint) of wine a day*".

Clearly since the beginning of human civilisation there has been and still is fertile soil for scepticism in medicine, especially before scientific evidence was available to determine rational practice. Peter Medawar when told of experimental results "too good to be true", commented *"curious, if it can be repeated independently it would be interesting"*. A measured sceptical response which left room for later modification if the facts demanded acceptance.

ORGAN TRANSPLANTATION

In the past 60 years science has bestowed many gifts to medicine, starting with safe anaesthesia which enabled new surgical treatments, in particular taking care of patients during operation without any natural function in their heart or lungs. The mechanical heart/lung machine allowed operations to be done unhurriedly on and inside the heart. At the same time surgeons were learning how to transplant organs, first the kidney and then the liver, heart, pancreas and intestines. Bone marrow was transplanted to save patients with lethal blood diseases.

Organ Transplantation passed through a fairly long phase of criticisms. As a medical student in the 1950s we were allocated patients with whom we had a special personal responsibility. I presented my case of a boy about my age who was dying of kidney failure. The senior consultant who was presiding said *"well you must make him comfortable but sadly he will be dead in two weeks"*. Without any background knowledge I asked could he not have a graft of a kidney, thinking in terms of horticulture. I was told no, and when I asked why not I was told *"it can't be done"*. By this time my colleagues were becoming concerned for my own future welfare and I was prodded in the ribs and told to shut up and not to ask any more stupid questions. Over coffee later we discussed the surgery that would be necessary to transplant a kidney and it seemed that there would need to be plumbing junctions of three vessels, an artery, a vein and the urine drainage tube, the ureter. Surgical techniques at that time could accomplish these tasks, so I was still baffled that my suggestion of a kidney graft was condemned out of hand. I had no idea of the phenomenon of graft rejection, a very powerful biological defence evolved to protect us from infections. Unfortunately tissue grafted from one individual to another is recognised as foreign by the body and destroyed as if it was an invading virus.

Medawar and his colleagues described the mechanism of rejection of skin grafts during the 2nd World War, since the subject was of great importance in the treatment of burns, particularly of aircraft crews. Surgical skin grafting was from one part of the body to another part of the same person, an "autograft", but it was also known that identical twins derived from the same egg would accept grafts from each other. The techniques of grafting skin were well established and some surgeons had looked into the feasibility of transplanting the kidney in experimental animals and showed that the kidney could withstand the surgical trauma of being removed and then transplanted with rapid restoration of its function, if the transplant operation was performed expeditiously and as with skin grafts, autotransplants were accepted indefinitely.

Medawar was asked if he could distinguish between identical and non-identical cattle twins. He felt this could be determined by skin grafting; identical twins would accept the twin's skin, non-identical calf twins would reject the twin's skin. The result of reciprocal skin grafting between both identical and non-identical cattle twins was a disappointment to the scientists, since the non-identical twins also accepted the skin grafts from their twin indefinitely. In trying to understand what had happened they felt that the anatomy and physiology of the bovine placenta could be the critical factor, since it is unique in that the circulation of one twin reciprocally crosses to that of the other. It had been shown previously that non-identical cattle twins often had red blood cells of different blood groups in the circulating blood, for example in man it would be the equivalent to having some red cells group A and some group B, which does not occur. It was postulated that in the developing foetus the immune system is not able to differentiate between self and non-self products.

Medawar felt that the phenomena was worthy of further investigation. He and his team found that exchange of tissue between incubating hens' eggs and tissue injected from one line of inbred mice into another during foetal development, rendered the animals that survived capable of accepting grafts from the donor of the tissue. The phenomenon was called "specific immunological tolerance", a result of foetal or neonatal exposure to prospective donor tissue. Although there was no obvious clinical application of the work the biological observations were extremely important and raised the question, "is there any way in which the immune system in adult life could be rendered similar to that in the foetus with plasticity to accept a graft, with the proviso that this would need to be only temporary so that normal immunity could protect the individual once the graft was established?" After 60 years we are still awaiting a positive solution to this question. At the time that these biological experiments were underway, Joseph Murray and his team of surgeons in Boston had in 1954 transplanted successfully a kidney between identical twins where the donor was healthy and the recipient was dying of kidney failure. This is by analogy the same as an autograft. The demonstration of successful surgical organ grafting to a patient brought the subject to the attention of physicians and surgeons worldwide.

If the operation could be done, why was it so difficult to prevent the inexorable rejection of a graft that occurs in virtually all transplants that are not between identical twins? Accidents from radioactive exposure and the devastation resulting from the atomic bomb destruction of Hiroshima and Nagasaki showed that bone marrow cells that produce red and white blood cells were especially vulnerable to gamma irradiation. Deprived of the white cells that are responsible for immune protection, patients subjected to irradiation of the bone marrow usually died but could in some circumstances be rescued by injection of un-irradiated bone marrow into the blood stream. The injected bone marrow cells have a natural tendency to home from the blood to the bone marrow and if they were taken from an identical twin they would re-populate the patient's immune and blood-forming system. There was a danger that bone marrow that was not perfectly matched would react against the recipient called a "graft-versus-host disease", which could be lethal but in some circumstances may be valuable in destroying leukaemia cells when bone marrow transplantation was used as therapy for leukaemic malignancy.

Surgeons wishing to develop kidney transplantation attempted to use irradiation to the whole body of the potential recipient to damage or destroy completely the immune system and then replace it with bone marrow from the potential donor. Unfortunately this led to disaster, the unprotected patients developing fatal infections and rejection of the organ graft could not be prevented. The almost 100% failure did not deter some surgeons from continuing with total body irradiation and this led to profound and justifiable scepticism from their colleagues. Only two patients were reported to have done well, and in each case they received a kidney from a non-identical twin and subsequently, as tissue typing became established, it was shown that the donor and the recipient were identically matched for the main tissue types which statistically would occur in 25% of sibling transplants. The tissue types are distinct from red blood groups which also need to be compatible. After much trial and error reliable techniques for tissue typing were established and they followed the rules of Gregor Mendel, so that between siblings 25% would be identical, 25% would have no factors in common and 50% would be half-matched.

Since irradiation was not shown to advance organ transplantation, alternative approaches were made. In 1959 I started research in England with 6-mercaptopurine, a drug used to treat leukaemia and found that it prolonged kidney graft survival in treated animals. The first trials of this compound and a close chemical derivative "Azathioprine" in patients was not very effective, but when cortisone was added there were some long-term good results of kidney transplantation and cautious attempts were made at liver and heart transplantation as the more complicated surgical techniques were developed to transplant these organs.

Some 20 years after the first use of Azathioprine and cortisone, another agent, Cyclosporine isolated from an earth fungus was shown to prolong survival of skin and organ grafts experimentally and its use by our group in Cambridge in patients increased the one year functional survival from 50% to 80%. For many years a cocktail of Azathioprine, cortisone and Cyclosporine was used in most centres, Cyclosporine being a watershed, liberating the transplant surgeons from oppressive scepticism which was quite shortly replaced by reluctant acceptance and then enthusiastic advocacy. Prior to Cyclosporine there were few centres worldwide seriously pursuing organ grafting but within two or three years of the introduction of Cyclosporine there were more than 1000, and good results were obtained in liver, heart and pancreas grafts.

Immunosuppression is still far from perfect. There was a phase of giving drug doses that were too large which had serious side-effects and now the move is towards minimal immunosuppression. The goal of tolerance when no maintenance immunosuppression will be necessary has not been reached except in a few cases of liver grafting, despite the study and trial of many new agents. Monoclonal antibodies, which selectively destroy the cells that cause rejection, have been introduced to the clinic. Recently a policy of pre-emptive induction has become popular, for example giving a powerful anti-lymphocyte monoclonal antibody "Campath" at the time of surgery, followed by a really low dose of maintenance drugs. The strategy has been called *"prope"* or almost tolerance. A very low dose of maintenance immunosuppression with few side effects may be sufficient for the wellbeing of the graft and the patient.

Although results are steadily improving, rejection, the side effects of the drugs, and the recurrence of the patient's original disease still cause failures. Nevertheless, patients have lived with good health and normal quality of life with the organ still functioning 40 years after kidney, liver and heart transplantation. With more than a million recipients of organ grafts worldwide, a major and increasing problem is the shortage of donor organs. The value of a life-saving organ to somebody otherwise doomed is more than any material wealth, so it is not surprising that the shortage has resulted in serious moral and ethical dilemmas, with accusations of criminal activity of stealing organs from patients having routine surgical treatment or even murder in order to obtain donors. Certainly there has been widespread exploitation by organ brokers in developing countries of poor people being paid for a kidney or a portion of the liver. Organs have been taken for transplantation for years from executed prisoners, especially in China. Medical tourism is an increasing activity but a travel expedition, depending on an execution, is considered morally wrong by major international and national scientific societies; despite these condemnations the practice continues.

It would seem that organ transplantation is a victim of its own success. The medical indications for an organ graft are becoming wider with older and sicker patients being considered, but the number of donors from road traffic accidents and brain haemorrhages is decreasing. Permission from their next of kin is often denied and the sceptics might justifiably claim that organ donor shortage is an insoluble problem.

GENETIC ENGINEERING AND STEM CELL THERAPIES

Genetic Engineering

It is now more than 60 years since the double helical structure of DNA was described with a clear indication of how the vital building blocks that synthesise proteins, the genes, resided in the nucleus of all cells and were replicated when the cells divided. The way in which the genetic alphabet of DNA is translated to the synthesis of complicated protein molecules is now understood, at least in principle. There is another intermediate alphabetic code of RNA that is essential in transmitting the signal of the gene to the manufacture of the protein. An array of essential participants in this process that express a gene to activity and switch it off have been identified and the whole genome of man has been described after a very laborious process, which initially was slow and expensive but now has been speeded up and becoming quite cheap. The code for individual genes can now be identified and I will discuss the goal of treating diabetes as an example of the approaches to gene and stem cell therapy.

The human insulin gene has been identified and can be isolated to reproduce in the cell of a bacterium as a so-called "plasmid" which is similar to a virus and about the same size. It is therefore possible to obtain very large numbers of copies of the gene. The plasmid can be incorporated into cells to persuade them to synthesise insulin. The plasmid may gain entrance, directly by the help of an electric current which opens up minute pores in the cell membrane or inside a virus which acts like a Trojan horse to take the plasmid into the cell in question. A liver, bone marrow or fat cell may be engineered to produce insulin but this is not enough to treat diabetes. A whole additional vital cell apparatus not fully understood is required to store insulin and release it only when it is needed when the blood sugar rises, as for example after a meal or a sugared drink. Release of insulin in the presence of low sugar can result in a dangerous and potentially lethal coma. As the various molecular processes of cell biology were unravelled, at each stage there has been uncritical media hype that treatment by genetic engineering is about to transform and cure previously untreatable diseases. Despite cautious attempts in the clinic more than 20 years ago, valuable therapy on a large scale has not yet materialised. A genetically engineered cell may not behave in the way the engineer intended, it may respond inappropriately or gradually lose its function. In the case of diabetes how would the control of the release of insulin be engineered?

Needless to say the sceptics have had a good time pointing to the inadequacies of not only the engineering techniques, but also the whole concept. Nevertheless some very rare diseases attributed to defects in one gene are beginning to show response to genetic engineering. The concept gets support from the fact that bone marrow and solid organ grafts all involve transfer of functioning genes.

STEM CELLS

The term stem cell is used loosely and often inaccurately. The perfect stem cell is a fertilised egg which will divide, proliferate and differentiate into a fully-formed foetus and eventually an adult individual. 30 years ago it was shown that at an early stage of cell division of the egg, each of the cells in an area called the inner cell mass of the blastocyst of the developing egg could be isolated and retained the capabilities of developing into a normal foetus. The cells are called "embryonic stem cells" and since they can produce any kind of tissue they are designated as pluripotent. Armed with this so-called "magic bullet" again there was speculation that embryonic stem cells, since they could in the laboratory produce cells of any type, might be used to repair and even replace damaged tissues and organs. The ability to manipulate on a minute scale cells in culture allowed the nucleus of the egg cell to be removed and replaced by the nucleus of a cell from any tissue. The nucleus itself contains the DNA genetic material and when transferred is capable of developing into a cloned individual. The first example regained world renown, as "Dolly" the cloned sheep. Other species have also been cloned, but to date attempts to clone monkeys have failed and there is a taboo on trying to clone humans. Individuals resulted from cloning may not have a normal lifespan and developmental abnormalities can occur. The techniques are tedious and only a small number of nuclear transfer attempts are successful.

The hopeful expectations led to a huge amount of money and effort to study the differentiation of embryonic stem cells and this added greatly to our knowledge of how the embryo develops from a single cell to a fully-formed foetus. Attempts have been made to nudge cells into a particular direction, for example towards the production of pancreatic beta cells, with a view to treatment of diabetes. This proved to be very difficult and only small numbers of cells have so far been produced with the characteristics of beta cells, which not only produce insulin but also store and regulate its release. If in the culture not all the cells are differentiated, following transplantation they can turn into tumours called teratomata and this is a worrying danger in the use of embryonic stem cells.

A very important biological observation was made in Japan in 2006 by Yamanaka and his colleagues, which showed that fully developed and differentiated adult cells, for example cells found in the skin, could be manipulated to de-differentiate and revert to a state similar to embryonic stem cells. If they could be used therapeutically they would have an important theoretical advantage since, they could be derived from the patient's own skin cells and therefore they would not be liable to rejection, which is a risk with embryonic stem cells, which have foreign tissue type antigens. Recently cells with similarities to iPS cells have resulted from treatment in culture with an acidic solution that is believed to stress them into a de-differentiated state.

The journey from an embryonic stem cell to, for instance, a pancreatic beta cell is complicated and currently the yield is low. The journey would be twice as long if the first phase is to dedifferentiate back to a state similar to an embryonic stem cell and then redifferentiate. Nevertheless this is an attractive line of research and it avoids ethical worries which have dogged embryonic stem cell research, which relies on sacrifice of a fertilised egg. A different and well-established stem cell treatment is bone marrow transplantation already mentioned. The transplantation of stem cells from the bone marrow can produce all the different types of blood-forming cells.

In the laboratory using special cultural techniques it is possible to turn bone marrow cells into other types of cells such as bone, cartilage, heart muscle, nerve cells and a difficult and complicated technique can result in the production of cells that secrete insulin, but so far only small numbers of such cells have been produced, nevertheless their function has been demonstrated by curing diabetic animals. The proof of principle is remarkable that certain bone marrow cells can be coaxed to produce insulin. To borrow from Dr. Johnson, the fact that a dog can be trained to walk badly on its hind legs is unusual but it is remarkable that it can do so at all! In all adult tissues there are probably stem cells; their role is not fully understood but may well be important in repairing damaged tissue. Much work is being done on stem cells in the brain, spinal cord and heart in attempts to mobilise them to repair and regenerate damaged central nervous or cardiac tissue. These efforts are still mainly in the experimental stage, with only cautious evidence-based studies in the clinic. Unfortunately, quack doctors interested in money, not science or helping patients, are offering untested "stem cell treatment" to desperate vulnerable patients. This gives serious science a bad name. There can be no doubt that safe and consistent techniques will eventually be developed. An early translation to the clinic seems unlikely but surprises occur, accidents happen which are not always harmful and eventually scepticism of these techniques will evaporate. It is up to scientists working in these areas to put the sceptics to flight, but currently scepticism encourages rigorous, repeatable scientific experiments that should discourage criminal exploitation. These optimistic thoughts would encourage the view of scepticism as a hero in science but the role of this two-edged sword can also turn to villain if it inhibits honest research.

Chapter VI

DISREGARD OF THE SANCTITY AND VALUE OF LIFE

Throughout history the value of life has been rated at different levels depending on prevailing culture and the belief in the value of human sacrifice. A parent will jump into a raging sea or enter a smoke-filled flaming house to rescue his or her child without any consideration of personal safety; warriors will obey orders, expecting almost certain death, but always with the miniscule chance that they may be extraordinary lucky. The idea of planning a mission in which self-destruction is part of the plot is more unusual and requires fatalistic dedication to the cause. In World War II Japanese pilots were prepared to attack enemy targets using their own planes as bombs filled with explosives, which would certainly destroy them as well as the enemy. This role was accepted as an honour to be a hero for the Emperor who had God-like status. More recently suicide bombers have frequently volunteered or been persuaded to volunteer with the full and certain knowledge that they will die, but they will be rewarded in heaven for this sacrifice. The amount of damage that can be done in this way is considerable as demonstrated with a new approach of destruction using passenger aeroplanes, full of fuel, as massive flame-throwing bombs which in the 9/11 attack on the

World Trade Twin towers in New York, killed 3000. The amount of death and destruction that can be caused by a few suicide bombers depends on what weapons are available. The use of a passenger plane was a completely novel approach to terrorism. Currently more deadly weapons, in particular those utilizing nuclear energy are not available in a suitable package for suicide bombers, but this could all change as technology advances and smaller, more compact atomic weapons are developed. No doubt new methods of destruction will be invented but from what is currently known, suicide bombers could not, on their own, wreak world calamity and such an approach in fact may not even be an objective of terrorist groups.

It would seem that a rogue state ruled by a mentally disturbed dictator should be regarded as the greatest danger, especially if he can interfere with the enemies' own communications and methods of weapons despatch. Immediate massive retaliation is the likely defence plan, but accidental unleashing of weapons and interference with the enemies' electronic network of defence is a serious possibility. There is a risk whenever human activity and decision making are involved that mistakes will be made, safeguards will be forgotten or fail-safe set-ups will not work perfectly. For major states with atomic weapons "playing poker" with rhetorical threats is an extremely dangerous game and very nearly led to disaster in the Cuban missile confrontation between America and the Soviet Union in October 1962. It would be unwise to assume that self-preservation and common sense would always prevail, since the human brain cannot be relied upon to act in a rational manner.

The consequences of the 'ratchet of science' driven by curiosity, often with no other motivation, has left us in a dangerous predicament. There is a risk that as the population pressure increases, especially when worthwhile jobs are not to be found to satisfy the need and honour of young people in impoverished states, aggressive political and religious confrontation will occur. It is unlikely that a state with atomic capability will voluntarily give it up, although if all atomic weapons were destroyed that would be the best solution for

World safety. In the meantime efforts must be increased to generate constructive dialogue between nations in the hope that no matter the reason, the final decision to unleash atomic weapons with the inevitable revenge and retribution, must be prevented and the risks reduced as far as is possible. Poison gas and biological weapons were not used in the second World War, although both sides had such weapons. Sadly more terrible atomic weapons were used against Hiroshima and Nagasaki and a repetition of this type of warfare with enhanced destructive capabilities of new weapons cannot be tolerated by any sane human or nation that values its own and others worth. The United Nations has a history of slow response and resolutions that are ignored and over-ridden by individual nations or leaders, who do not recognise or respect the authority.

For an optimistic appraisal one could point out that for each year that goes by without an atomic attack, world opinion will become stronger in its resolve to avoid such a disaster, but while the weapons exist there is no room for complacency.

LONERS AND CULTS

The Japanese author Haruki Murakami wrote a fascinating and disturbing in-depth investigation into the Tokyo underground terrorist attack with the nerve gas Sarin in 1995. The terrorist plot was hatched by a sect of more than 1000 followers of a pseudo-religious anarchist guru, Shoko Asahara, whose main philosophy seemed to be to destroy the peaceful normal society of contemporary Japanese life. The people recruited to the sect appeared to be remarkably normal with little in the way of previous mental disease or dissatisfaction with Japanese politics or society. The spectrum of those joining the sect was wide with a number of University graduates, including physicians, physicists and chemists. They were indoctrinated and worked away, synthesising supplies of Sarin, extraordinarily unobserved or interfered with by the police or other authorities. How they managed to operate below the normal surveillance "radar" is difficult to understand. The chemists and engineers manufactured their own Sarin in packages of liquid in plastic bags. The plan was to open the bags in several trains on different underground lines of the very complicated and extensive Japanese metro railway system at a co-ordinated time to cause the maximum chaos, damage and death of completely innocent citizens. The attitude to the plot, expressed to Murakami by some of the participants was very strange. One middle-aged woman, waiting to unleash her bag of Sarin, was sitting in a carriage opposite a young mother with a small child. Observing this woman with a small child, the would-be terrorist felt how sweet and loving they were and had profound sympathy for them, but this kind and civilised train of thought in no way disturbed her resolve to obey the commandments of the terrorist guru to open the bag of poison, which she did. The heroism of many of the commuters in the trains and especially the authorities running the railway system was impressive, despite the complete surprise of this horrific attack. First aid, medical and paramedical support and help were swiftly brought into action and as a result many victims survived, after the authorities understood the nature of the poison and had medication with which to combat it. Murakami tried, with many interviews of some of the perpetrators, to comprehend why they had joined the sect and how they were prepared to be loyal to the sect even when they were expected to commit murder on people they had never previously come across. Having drifted into the sect, the individuals became more and more involved and presumably brainwashed by the guru and his assistants, until they felt that they were part of the mission to destroy fellow citizens.

The terrorist attack in Norway in 2011 by a single individual was unprecedented in the number of people he killed and injured. Behring Breivik appeared to be motivated by political racial concepts and had been in touch with extreme right wing groups in other countries. He was able to amass an armoury of weapons and explosives, and again it was the extreme surprise, viciousness and apparently unmotivated destruction he wrought that took the authorities off guard. At his trial psychiatrists were unable to find any well-defined psychiatric illness and indeed the man himself denied that he was abnormal and did not show any psychiatric symptoms. How he came to have such terrible feelings, which were translated into killing action is, to most people, incomprehensible and he showed no remorse and his attitude appeared to be devoid of normal humanity.

In 1966 another "loner" killer was Charles Whitman, an ex-marine in Austin, Texas. In this case he had premonitions and dreadful feelings that he needed to kill somebody and he was worried about this and went to his doctor, who could find no abnormality and referred him to a psychiatrist who was unable to make a psychiatric diagnosis. These terrifying feelings of wishing to kill continued and one day he took a gun and shot his mother, went into the University of Texas campus, climbed a tower and shot and killed 14 students and injured another 40 before a police marksman killed him. When his belongings were searched there was a note requesting that if he was killed could the authorities arrange for a careful post-mortem examination to be carried out. The autopsy revealed a small, malignant tumour in the centre of the brain in the amygdala area which is thought to be the centre of many emotional activities of the brain. So this patient was ill and behaved as a terrorist criminal. He had a well-defined brain tumour which is an unusual finding in this type of random killing. How to diagnose and manage such cases is not clear.

The Waco Davidians religious sect terrorist episode and massacre in 1993, again in Texas, has similarities to the Sarin Tokyo underground attack and like that, it was associated with pseudo-religious brainwashing by a guru, Vernon Wayne Howell, who changed his name to David Koresh and believed and persuaded his followers to believe that he was a prophet and challenged society with violence.

The 2013 Boston marathon bombers were unusual in that the murderers came from Chechen, which had suffered and been involved in the long and bloody dispute with the Russian republic. Many terrorist acts had featured in the conflict, including the killing of the audience in a Moscow theatre. However, the longstanding conflict was not in any way involved with America. In fact if anything the Americans had leant on the side of the Chechen community rather than the Russian government. The two young men had come to America as an adopted country, presumably for a better life, but slowly the elder brother became indoctrinated in hatred of the American way of life and developed a feeling that as a devout religious Muslim he should fight against it. He travelled back to Chechen and spent a considerable time with terrorist groups and in the course of this visit his hatred of America became intensified and when he came back to Boston, his strong personality influenced his younger brother and they joined together to plan their murderous terrorist attack, making their own bombs with a recipe, apparently available on the internet. Again an illustration of how science in the digital age can be communicated to anyone who happens to be interested. The brothers had planned a series of attacks but the ubiquitous CCTV cameras enabled the authorities to identify the individuals as local inhabitants with a number of associates and friends, who recognised them. They had always regarded the brothers as pleasant individuals, and both of them had done well at school. The younger brother was a medical student and both had excelled in martial arts, one as a boxer and the other as a wrestler. How such intense hatred could be translated into practical terrorism in a young mind is very difficult for outsiders to comprehend. In two books, "The Islamist" and "The Reluctant Fundamentalist", attempts have been made by the two Muslim authors to explain how indoctrination from peer groups and training in terrorist camps, especially in Pakistan, appear to be able to recruit volunteers to perpetrate terrorist violence on fellow citizens with no stirring of their consciences. The murders are considered by the terrorists as truly holy acts, which will be rewarded in heaven if they die as suicide martyrs. Advances in science were utilised and translated into warped human activity of bomb-making, fuelled by intense hatred of fellow citizens by the perpetrators. One terrorist interviewed on television explained how he perceived things. He stated "in the West you love life, we however love death".

Chapter VII

THE SKY IS THE LIMIT:
ROCKETS AND COSMOLOGY

"We live in an age of guided missiles and misguided men"

Martin Luther King

Ever since the beginning of recorded history there has been fascination of the sun, the moon and the stars. They have been regarded as omens of good and bad fortune and have been bestowed with god-like powers. The sun figured centrally in ancient Egypt and buildings were constructed to direct its rays to demonstrate the religious significance by illuminating sacred sculptures and portions of buildings at certain times. The rising sun also had great relevance to the Japanese. Scholars studied the heavenly bodies carefully and made remarkably accurate observations despite having no telescopes. The practical significance of astronomy was utilised in navigation, by all maritime nations.

The magical and astrological predictions of the heavenly bodies merged with scientific observations and since the two were not separated during medieval times there was much confusion between what was observed and mythological astrological interpretations. The Aristotalion geocentric theory was accepted and it fitted into commonsense observations and was conveniently adopted as religious dogma. Copernicus challenged this view and was extremely cautious in expressing his theories, which happened to be helpful to the Church in renovation of the Gregorian calendar. He died on the day of the publication of his major opus. His argument that the sun is the centre of our universe intrigued a number of scholars, in particular Galileo, who had constructed simple telescopes and was able to record far more accurate observations than had been possible previously. Despite treading very carefully Galileo was punished by the Inquisition and was considered lucky to avoid execution; he was sentenced to permanent house arrest. Increasingly accurate observations attested to the correctness of the Copernican hypothesis.

In the early 20th century the vastness of the observable universe began to be apparent and this naturally led to extreme controversy concerning its origin. Movements of the stars were recorded and all were travelling away from each other and our planet, shifting the spectrum of light to the red end suggesting that the universe was expanding. This hypothesis was strongly advocated by the American astronomer, Edwin Hubble. There were a number of alternative theories additional to that expressed in the Bible. Most debate centred round the two popular views amongst cosmologists, namely that the universe was in a steady state on the one hand or that it arose in an explosive instant of "singularity" of infinite mass and heat as the so-called "Big Bang". This was followed by a cosmic inflation faster than the speed of light and a plethora of consequences emanating from the "Bang" currently observed in the behaviour of stars and galaxies. The concept of the "Big Bang" was the logical deduction of all celestial observations that could be traced backwards in time. The hypothesis was clarified by a Belgian Catholic priest, Georges Lemaitre. Before the "Big Bang" we know nothing and can believe anything. Opinion now favours the "Big Bang" theory with the continuing expansion of the universe. Recent evidence points to the expansion accelerating, which was not expected.

The modern study of cosmology is dependant on increasingly powerful telescopes based on visual observation and also via radio waves collected on different sensors linked together.

A new dimension available to cosmologists is the introduction of space exploration. This depended directly on the scientific efforts of German rocket specialists during World War II. They were developing a rocket weapon and an important technological advance was introduced by Werner von Braun of the liquid rocket fuel that propelled the V2 weapons against southern England. With the end World War II von Braun moved to the United States and became head of rocket science devoted to improvement of missiles as weapons but gradually peaceful application became envisaged. German scientists also collaborated with Russian experts in producing a rocket that propelled the first Earth-orbiting satellite "Sputnik" in 1957. In 1961 the Soviet scientists followed with the first successful manned orbiting space craft piloted by Yuri Gagarin. The success of these launchings surprised the Americans who began to devote far more effort into space exploration, and an extremely well-financed lunar "Apollo" programme succeeded in landing astronauts on the moon in 1969 and bringing them back safely. Neil Armstrong, one of the astronauts famous quote from the moon was prophetic "that's one small step for man, one giant leap for mankind". The stage was now set for accurate launching of satellites that could be programmed for as variety of tasks, especially transmitting information for navigation, surveillance of features and activity on Earth and, with increasingly powerful cameras, probing into distant stars and planets. Satellite communication is now central to many activities, both civilian and military and numerous satellites are orbiting the world. Some have broken up by accident or according to the design and there is now much litter in space which constitutes a danger to other satellites including manned space craft.

Activity probing space continues to accelerate. In 2013 the Chinese successfully landed a rover probe on the moon and the European Space Agency after years of skilled technological endeavour produced a 1 billion pixel camera which they have recently launched. This huge telescopic camera called "Gaia" after the Greek Goddess of the Earth, is on its way to probe our own galaxy, the Milky Way and to provide information on 1 billion stars, providing a 3D map of the stars and data on historical previous positions and activity of stars and those predicted for the future. This Milky Way 3D mapping project is expected to clarify many currently controversial theories and will probably introduce new ones.

All this space activity reflects genuine curiosity and fascination that is part of human nature throughout history. At every stage the new information that has been gathered has potential for improving at least the convenience of our modern civilisation but also the advances in rocket and spacecraft technology have obvious military significance. Ever since the launch of Sputnik space exploration has had international importance, conferring great prestige on the participating nations.

New Weapons of War and How We Might Learn to Control Them

Gunpowder invented by the Chinese for fireworks was appropriated by Western powers to make cannons. This was a game change in the pursuit of war. Coating cannonballs with graphite increased the range and accuracy and provided the British with superior firepower on land and at sea. Seemingly small technical improvements in ship design and construction, better ropes, more efficient pulleys, improved sail management all increased the effectiveness of ships as war weapons. The rifling of gun barrels evolved in Europe in the 15th-17th centuries further increased the accuracy and range of new guns, conferring a temporary advantage to the initiators until the invention became widely adopted.

The Napoleonic Wars and the American Civil War both mobilised huge armies which became locked in terrible conflict with enormous casualties of killed and hideously wounded. Carnage on an even larger scale occurred in the trench warfare of the 1914-18 Great War. New spin-offs from science and technology produced chlorine, mustard poison gas and the armoured tank, which was overwhelming in its superiority against horse cavalry. High-explosive bombing from the air, increased the casualties and many civilians also suffered. The horrific burns and blindness following the release of poisonous gases caused general revulsion and following international agreement persuaded opposing forces to avoid the use of chemical weapons. This has not stopped development of new chemical weapons. The nerve gas Sarin was used by terrorists in the Japanese underground attack in 1995. Ricin derived from castor oil seeds, has been used in Secret Service killings. A small injection causes delayed lethal poisoning for which there is no remedy. The use of bacteria and viruses as weapons has been developed secretly in a number of countries. There is no doubt in the efficacy of such an approach to killing, but there remains the difficulty in the distribution of the poison or infectious agents and keeping them confined to the enemy. Back-firing of the attack occurred, when the wind changed after the release of poison gas on the Western Front in the first World war. Perhaps the most repellent and disgusting agent so far employed was the poisoning of a Russian diplomat, Alexander Litvinenko, in London by a radioactive element, Polonium, which has no taste and once ingested spreads through the body, emitting lethal alpha rays which do not contaminate other people, but lead to a slow and painful death; there is no effective treatment. The course of this poor man's demise was graphically demonstrated on British television from day to day, ending only with him perishing. The Botulin toxin, used in small amounts as "Botox" to remove wrinkles as a cosmetic medication, does so by paralysing muscle and in large amounts is lethal. Poisonous bacteria Clostridium botulinum and Anthrax have been sent in parcels and envelopes as a form of assassination but so far have not been very effective.

Bacteria resistant to antibiotics as a result of mutations are potential weapons. For example antibiotic resistant Mycobacterium tuberculosis introduced into drinking water reservoirs could cause rampant untreatable disease in an unprotected population.

VIRUS WEAPONS

In 1919 there was a catastrophic influenza epidemic, killing millions of people, more deaths than occurred as a result of the hostilities of the 1914-18 war. There is genuine fear that virologists could construct a new influenza virus with similar deathly potential that would spread from human to human and with the current volume of air travel throughout the world, might be more devastating than the 1919 epidemic. The 2002-2003 SARS (severe acute respiratory syndrome) epidemic proved to be very difficult to manage and caused dreadful lung disease, particularly in Asia. So much fear was generated that a few doctors caring for afflicted patients were banned by their relatives to return home for fear of spreading the disease to their loved ones. A few such cases reported were a small percentage of the medical and nursing profession, most of whom were self-quarantined and continued heroically to care for the sick.

Governments and international scientific bodies have been concerned at the possibility of using viruses as weapons. The danger perceived is that international terrorist organisations might, if they had the facilities and the knowledge, modify lethal viruses to infect an enemy using, for example, smallpox, certain strains of contagious flu, Ebola and Marburg. There is concern that open ethical studies of these viruses, at the molecular and gene level, could be adapted and modified as weapons, thus there have been government pressure and voluntary international agreements for embargos on research that was perceived to have a threat. Unfortunately this also slows up research that could help in eliminating diseases with new vaccines. An attempt was made to destroy all sources of the virulent smallpox virus but the counter argument is that this would interfere with methods of controlling an unexpected or deliberately targeted outbreak with a secretly modified virus. The dilemma is similar to the central concept of this book. How much control should there be of genuine ethical scientific investigation and at what stage does this control become counterproductive? Should scientists, before embarking on research on a certain subject, carefully consider the pros and cons of their research leading to good or evil sequelae? Naturally governments will be very interested in what studies are ongoing and also whether they should be permitted and there will be many considerations that are secret because of their sensitive nature and strategic importance. As with most of the other Chapters in this book it has to be accepted that once data are out in the public domain they cannot be put back and unlearned. Perhaps increased awareness of the "ratchet" effect of science may be of value in controlling undesirable and dangerous spin-offs that can be adapted into weapons.

Chapter VIII

THE NEXT PHASE

"War is a contest between the brains, imagination, inventiveness and teamwork of the scientists"

James Collip 1943

3-D PRINTING

Desktop inkjet and laser printers have become smaller and cheaper and the concept of printing in three dimensions has been around for more than 30 years. Charles W. Hull in California in 1984 took out a patent in which three dimensional objects can be created using multiple thin layer deposits that can be solidified on digital designs. There have been numerous modifications, improvements and developments to simplify 3D printing, which has a remarkable versatility in the materials that can be used, adding to a support thin layers of the material chosen which can also be coloured. Many different techniques have been tried but the inkjet principle is currently the most popular. 3-D printing can be a commercial service of a firm instructed to copy a three dimensional model, which can be produced to order and collected or mailed. Alternatively the actual printing process can be done at home or in the office using 3D printers which are now becoming small and affordable. The whole object may be produced or just component parts which are later put together. Even at this stage there are multiple uses from constructing replacement body parts, especially bones, making jewellery, tools, car prototypes, and even human models for which the customer sends multiple self-portraits to the company that will then send back a small sculptured "Selfie" manikin of that person.

An interesting development being explored is to produce food by 3-D printing that can be eaten. The impact of science on food has been enormous, enabling many edible products to be preserved almost indefinitely by freezing and whole meals are packaged and frozen as commercial items. This approach to food will be facilitated by 3D printing. The idea is popular in many catering companies and the appearance of the product may be extremely enticing but the element that seems to be forgotten is taste, which used to be one of the main attractions of food. A good taste is still dependent on fresh products and individual effort and passion on the part of the cook. Personalised cooking by dedicated chefs using fresh materials is time-consuming but brings out the genuine taste. I think it is unlikely that 3D printing or artificial meat production will ever supplant traditional cooking. However, many people do not seem to care too much what they eat, and are targets to be brain-washed by advertisers with dubious claims often supplemented with "stage" performances by waiters taking orders in expensive restaurants to justify the grossly overpriced bill. Yet many rich customers in chic restaurants do not mind being conned.

As has been the theme of this book, most inventions, no matter the original motive, will be scrutinised as to whether they might produce weapons and 3D printing is no exception. The plastic parts of a working 3D gun which would evade current airport security are already available and no doubt will be developed further and 3D printing can also produce a metal gun. It seems that there is an almost limitless number of materials that can be utilised in 3D printing which currently is in its infancy and will have multiple ramifications in both civilian and military applications (Figure 20).

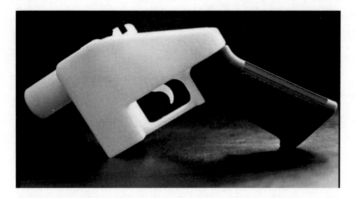

Figure 20a. Plastic working gun, components constructed by 3D printing. This weapon would be difficult to detect by airport security.

Figure 20b. Metal gun. Also produced by 3D printing using layers of metal powder.

DRONES

In biology drones are the male bees that have only one function and that is to impregnate the queen. In modern warfare the drone's function is quite different. During World War II unmanned flying bombs were developed by the Germans as V1 weapons with wings and flew like conventional planes. They could not be directed accurately to the target and eventually they were perceived by the allies to be slow enough to be destroyed by anti-aircraft artillery and were intercepted by modern fighter planes that were able to pick them off very effectively. The V2 weapon was entirely different. This was rocket-propelled and was the forerunner of modern missiles, and provided the power for satellite deployment and space exploratory rockets. The V2 shot into space but its return was unpredictable and inaccurate, it could not be intercepted but caused severe random damage. The V2 onslaught had a serious demoralising effect on the population, since there was no way of telling where the rockets would land.

The idea of a radio-controlled aircraft became a practical device between the first and second World Wars and was used extensively by the Royal Navy as a target for naval artillery. Just before the second World War an American Admiral was invited by the Royal Navy to witness the use of the Royal Naval drones for target practice. He considered this was a very interesting demonstration and was worthy of development, not as a target but as a weapon for both surveillance and aggression.

Drone warfare is a very important strategic weapon as control of the flight of the drone has now become extremely precise with relayed images of the potential targets displayed on a television screen that can be anywhere in the world and quite often on a different continent from the target. The largest and most powerful drones can take off from and land on aircraft carriers and carry powerful missile weapons. Recently "predator" drones with "hellfire" missiles have been deployed which have an extensive and deadly capability (Figure 21). Despite remarkable accuracy there will always be collateral damage and many civilians have been killed. The drone operators often in places distant from the attack are prone to suffer from severe post-traumatic stress disorder, especially aggravated by the recurring, haunting feeling that they have killed women and children they did not know in another continent without getting themselves into any personal danger in this process of trans-continental assassination.

Figure 21. US Predator drone firing as Hellfire Missile. Unmanned attack controlled remotely.

The monitoring by surveillance drones has become exceedingly efficient. Some of them are little larger than a big insect and, although these mini-drones cannot deliver a lethal attack, they can be directed through small entrances and windows and send information back and guide an effective weapon to a target.

The use of drones in lethal aggression is becoming increasingly successful and in surveillance activity they will be used in the future to obtain information, both for international spying but also in commercial sabotage.

For a nation fearing attack there are a variety of options that could be developed in an attempt to retaliate. There are a number of different systems of defence rockets which can bring down an approaching missile by targeting it in the sky. To date some of these have been effective but, inevitably, also some missiles will always evade the defence and get through. So what other options can be explored? Each of the new scientific killing machines requires a complicated electronic control. This network depends on a source of electricity and very intricate hardware and software. There is much reliance on orbiting satellites for information and pin-pointing targets, so how vulnerable are these electronic control networks to destruction or interference? There have been speculations that an assault from space on the main electricity grid system of a nation could result in its malfunction. Another approach is to hack into the enemy's computer system, and internet access, which might also provide an opportunity to confuse and terrify civilian and military populations with threats and misinformation. As soon as a new hacking technique is developed, retaliatory defences are rapidly introduced to make that hacking ineffective or at least difficult, but rather like regulations on tax avoidance or prevention of unlawful immigration, no sooner is one loophole closed than another is opened. In terms of warfare this intellectual competition could have fearful consequences. Science has spawned all these new methods of killing, so it would not be unreasonable to expect science to come up with new ways of keeping the world safe, but as long as atomic weapons are available there is a danger that they may be used by a rogue state in the hands of an unbalanced dictator, or just a most terrible mistake or accident in calculation of a perceived threat with immediate or even pre-emptive retaliation. Perhaps for the sake of humanity we should speedily establish institutes for the scientific maintenance of peace, recruiting high quality staff from all sciences to devise a means to enhance peaceful brain activity and suppress aggression. This would give the appointed brain manipulators a very difficult task. Even if they had a medication that would do the job, how could it be utilised in practice?

CYBER WARFARE AND CYBER TERRORISM

The smooth running of civilian society and the maintenance of an alert and fully prepared military apparatus are both highly dependent on electricity supply and computer function. Even a small local cut in electricity can put a large international airport completely out of action and similarly crashing of a computer network can halt transport, both in the air and on the railways. As with new technologies in the operating theatre when something goes wrong, there is no back-up of experts trained in the old methods of management. Without reliance on computers air traffic control is completely impotent and without electricity the same applies to almost all activities involved in transport, including the loss of computer control of networks, satellite navigation and surveillance. It is therefore not surprising that this soft underbelly of civilisation is a perfect target for future aggression. A nation could be brought to its knees unless it has really robust, failsafe auxiliary facilities.

To target and interfere with the internet activities of enemies and commercial competitors is becoming increasingly effective and constitutes a severe danger. A well-organised cyber attack could bring to a standstill computer activities and the military and civilian organisation of an enemy nation. The recent publicity into phone hacking of celebrities and politicians in the UK and then the revelation of the extraordinary scale of the collection of data, including from the personal mobile telephones of heads of state, Angela Merkl and Francois Hollande, appears to be only the tip of the iceberg revealed by the whistleblower, Edward Snowden. Of course nations will spy on each other and the internet greatly facilitates espionage, particularly when data are collected and used by huge organisations such as Google, Facebook and Twitter. The rest of the material Snowden has taken from the secret computer archives of the United States will no doubt provide more evidence of the huge extent of this so-called "prism" secret data collecting enterprise. Naturally the US Government is aghast and furious at Edward Snowden's whistle-blowing, but there is an inevitability that this type of revelation will occur sooner or later in almost any kind of covert enterprise when large numbers of people have access to secret files. The activity itself is so extensive that this risk must be accepted, although governments strive to change frequently and improve the security, safeguards and codes to try to minimise the dangers.

A new possible aggressive threat is from an e bomb generating an electromagnetic pulse (EMP) to disable electricity installations and their distribution, which would paralyse the internet and all vital activities of a nation. To interfere with electricity supplies would be a crippling blow without a single shot being fired. Great efforts are being made by experts in all powerful nations to control and prevent these threats from materialising but as soon as one avenue is closed another opens. Some of the people involved are extremely skilled and clever so the aggressive Cyber "chess game" will continue indefinitely.

COMPUTER VIRUSES

The possibility of disrupting computers in a covert manner appears to have been fulfilled in reality, with the "stuxnet" virus that required enormous resources to produce and attacked Iran's nuclear programme in 2010 causing severe damage. This appeared to be aided by another virus called "duqu".

A powerful cyber espionage virus "Flame" remained undetected in computers like a Trojan Horse for five years before it started to gather data files and changed settings on computers to disrupt and eavesdrop on the communications that were going through the computer. Naturally the details on these espionage malware are secret and probably so complicated that only a nation state could invent and distribute them. They have the enormous power of disabling strategic computer activity and could undermine the defences of a nation.

CODA

Curiosity and the quest for knowledge are part of human nature. Looking at science in its broadest sense it would be difficult not to conclude that these human attributes are central to human behaviour in the context of all historical assessments (Figure 22). The peaceful consequences of scientific curiosity have undoubtedly improved the quality of life for the majority of human beings, raising the horizons of enjoyment and fulfilment way beyond the minimal need for food, water, shelter and reproduction On the other hand applications of science for more efficient pursuit of violence and war are self-evident and unfortunately this scientific development has had alarming consequences in the recent past and acceleration in this direction seems to be unstoppable. In Max Born's letter to his son the shock of thermo-nuclear explosions in Japan and the realisation that these would not have been possible without intense scientific activity nevertheless led him to an optimistic outlook. He felt that scientific devices of destruction would be held in check because "man had a heart".

I have not made any attempt to consider the arts side of humanity nor the separation of the two cultures into arts and science that was the theme of C.P. Snow's book "The Two Cultures" . The culture of compassion, a code of ethics and a feeling of kindness and concern for other humans and the need to protect the animal and plant life of the earth are important to most people and their leaders, but despite these wishes, population increases, resources diminish, species are lost and aggression continues.

Figure 22. Pandora – all but one of the Furies have escaped when she succumbed to curiosity of opening the casket. Only "Hope remains". Painting by John Waterhouse

There is an overwhelming need for those who determine political and scientific policy to beware of and avoid decisions that could be translated into uncontrollable violence so that science will continue to benefit people worldwide. Vigilance and continuous appraisal of new knowledge and potential applications may justify a cautiously, optimistic view. Humans have "a heart" as pointed out by Max Born and also the power of reasoning. These two together should combine beneficially for decision-making and actions that will not totally abandon us to *que sera sera*, without an attempt on our part to direct "what will be" towards a creed of to "live and let live".

The aim of this book has been to describe some of the advances in science and how these impinge on society with the emphasis on the ratchet nature of scientific knowledge and also our inability to predict the applications of science. There is no way in which the ratchet can be dismantled and inevitably new knowledge will spawn good and also potentially bad results. Science designed to produce new and more powerful weapons, may have unexpected beneficial civilian applications. The manner in which human nature is genetically determined controls the interaction between new knowledge and how it is used. Compassionate co-existence between peoples is threatened by natural tendencies of aggression, fuelled by religion and politics and is susceptible to being hijacked by crazy psychopaths. There seems to be no escaping the conclusion that the best we can do is to examine carefully the *status quo* and endeavour repeatedly to reinforce the need for peaceful co-existence if *Homo sapiens* is to survive and flourish rather than face the possibility of *Homo extinctus.*

GLOSSARY

INTRODUCTION

Lise Meitner (1878-1968), Austrian born mathematician and physicist who worked with Max Planck and Otto Hahn and was the first to use the word "fission" to describe the splitting of a uranium atom subjected to neutron bombardments. (L Meitner, OR Frisch. Disintegration of Uranium by Neutrons: A new type of nuclear reaction. Letters to the Editor, Nature Feb 11. 1939). Because of her Jewish origins she was forced to leave Berlin and during the 2nd World War lived in Sweden. She resisted attempts to recruit her for the Manhattan Project and repeatedly stated "I will have nothing to do with a bomb". Her co-worker, Otto Hahn, was awarded a Nobel Prize. She received many honours and had a new element named after her, "Meitnerium109". Einstein referred to her as "our German Marie Curie". After the war she moved to Cambridge to join family members there. Her scientific papers were archived in Churchill College.

Paul Bowersox, A regular contributor to the nuclear café blog, he wrote a dedication to Lise Meitner quoted in the text.

Los Alamos, in New Mexico, where the nuclear bomb research was concentrated as part of the Manhattan Project.

Tim Berners-Lee (b.1955), Computer scientist working at CERN in Switzerland. He invented the "World Wide Web" and dedicated it for the benefit of mankind and did not make any attempt to file a patent.

Edward Snowden (b. 1983), US computer scientist who defected from his top secret involvement in the extensive recording of personal data and transactions in the digital world, including the hacking of mobile phones of heads of state, Angela Merkel and Frances Hollande. As a whistle blower he fled to Hong Kong having divulged some of the secret material to the Observer newspaper in England. He left Hong Kong for asylum in Russia as he was being pursued by US authorities for divulging state secrets. Apparently he is still in Russia and new material which he has collected appears from time to time in the media.

Anna Middleton – Senior Ethics Researcher and genetic councillor at the Sanger Institute, Cambridge.

Louis Pasteur (1823-1895), French Medical scientist, famous for his development of an anti-rabies vaccine and making milk safe from tuberculosis contamination by heating, a process that became known as 'pasteurisation'. A proponent of the Germ Theory of disease.

CERN, Switzerland – Pan-European, huge underground installation to study the acceleration of particles and their high speed collision in experimental physics.

Charles Darwin (1809-1882), English naturalist, who devoted his life to studying the biology of animals and plants to construct the theory of evolution that revolutionised biological thinking.

Adolf Hitler (1889-1945), Dictator of German Third Reich, elected democratically but the whole democratic process was subsumed into a vicious dictatorial regime with a brutal record of anti-semitic murder in the Holocaust. Hitler originally wished to be a painter and according to legend he competed to be accepted at the Vienna Academy of Arts but his application was unsuccessful; the winner was Egon Schiele. If Egon Schiele had not been a candidate world history might have been very different.

Stone, Bronze and Iron Ages - These three phases have been used by archaeologists and historians to describe the central pattern of development of early man up to recorded history. Roughly - Stone Age pre-2000BC, Bronze Age 2000-800BC, Iron Age 1800BC onwards.

"Spinning Jenny" (1764) A mechanical machine invented by James Hargreaves in Lancashire, to facilitate weaving using multiple wool and cotton spools.

Robert Oppenheimer (1904-1967) Polymath, mathematician and physicist who headed the Manhattan Project. His learning was legendary; it was said that as a child he asked his cousin to question him in Latin which he answered in Ancient Greek. He had an unstable personality and was accused of attempting to poison his chief, Professor Patrick Blackett in Cambridge with an apple laced with cyanide. In the course of the Manhattan Project he quoted from the ancient Hindu sacred work the Bhagavad Gita, "Now I have become death, destroyer of the world", a quote ascribed to the god Krishna.

CHAPTER 1

Albert Einstein (1879-1955) German Theoretical Physicist. Nobel Prize winner famous for the Mass-Energy Equivalent formula, $E=MC2$ and the general theory of relativity.

Max Born (1882-1970) German mathematical physicist who initially worked in Gottingen, but later in Edinburgh. His statistical analysis of quantum physics were pioneering and contrary to Einstein's views yet Born and Einstein were friends and indulged in extensive correspondence together. Born recognised immediately the dilemma of scientists whose work pursued out of curiosity was nevertheless used to produce weapons, in particular the splitting of the atom, leading to the thermonuclear weapons used against Japan.

Gustav Born (b.1921) son of Max Born. Medical scientist who studied the victims of the atomic bomb attacks in Japan. Emeritus Prof. of Pharmacology at Kings College, London.

Bertrand Russell (1872-1970) Philosopher, mathematical logician, essayist and social critic. Nobel Prize winner in Literature.

Joseph Rotblat (1908-2005) Nuclear physicist, worked on the Manhattan Project and resigned on moral grounds. Nobel Peace Prize.

Leo Szilard (1898-1964) Hungarian-American physicist, conceived the nuclear chain reaction, worked on the Manhattan Project, resigned on moral grounds.

Nikita Khrushcev (1894-1971) Led Soviet Union during Cold War.

Damascus, Arkansas (1980) Site of Titan II missile accidental explosion.

Chernobyl, An explosion at Chernobyl Nuclear power station in northern Ukraine in 1986 caused huge loss of life and illness from radiation-cancers, leukaemia, genetic mutations and cardiovascular disease.

Fukushima In 2011 explosion in a Japanese nuclear power station caused by an earthquake followed b y a devastating tsunami.

Ronald Reagan (1911-2004) 40th President of the USA from 1981-1989.

Polaris missiles Two stage solid fuel nuclear-armed submarine-launched ballistic missile first fired in 1960.

Armageddon Book of Revelation, Ancient Greek word which has come to mean the end of the world through war or natural disaster.

CHAPTER II

Piraha An Amazonian tribe of around 150 individuals who are successful hunter/gatherers. Anthropologists and missionaries attempted to understand their culture and were surprised that they were unable to discover any words or concepts for yesterday, tomorrow, numbers or colours and they did not appear to have any religion of their own. Missionaries asked if they would subscribe to Christianity and one of the Elders asked the missionary if he had seen Jesus. When the missionary responded that he had not, the Piraha told him that in that case he would not worship him.

Battle of Crecy (1346) In northern France, sited a bitter battle between the French and Italians on one side and the British on the other.

Sumerians Ancient semitic inhabitants of Mesopotamia in present day Iraq. They developed a writing system with wedge-shaped strokes known as cuneiform. They lived in the city of Ur, the first known civilised city.

Francis Crick (1916-2004) and **James Watson (b.1928)** – the two collaborating mathematical physicists in Cambridge who discovered the molecular structure of the DNA. Their task was aided considerably by the crystallographer Rosalyn Franklyn (1920-1958), who worked in King's College, London and produced the first X-ray defraction photograph of the DNA molecular recognized by Watson as a double helix.

Mohamed Morsi Egypt's first democratically elected President in 2012. His presidency was overturned in 2013 when the army once more took over.

Greek Oil Flaming projectile weapon developed by the Greeks with secrets of its recipe and projection kept from the Islamic opponents in the siege of Constantinople in 700AD. As long as the secret was intact this gave the Christians considerable advantage in sea warfare.

The British East India Company (1612-1757) became an extremely powerful trading enterprise with a large army and colonial administration, especially in India, the Malay Straits territories and other parts of South East Asia. The Dutch East India Company was similar, especially active in the Indonesian archipelago.

The Renaissance (17th & 18th Centuries). The name given to the period when new learning started to make its observations known and accepted based on scientific studies, and observations, particularly using the microscope and telescope. Those involved were in considerable danger of persecution by the Inquisition if the findings did not tally with the Church's interpretations.

Niccolo Machiavelli (1469-1527) Courtier and writer of the 16th Century whose most famous book "The Prince" published 1532 explains the conniving and corruption inevitable in obtaining power in medieval Italy. "It would be best to be both loved and feared, but since the two rarely come together, anyone compelled to choose will find greater security in being feared than loved". His most famous quote.

Giordana Bruno (1548-1600) Priest who was controversial in his interpretation of the Bible and Catholic texts. He was subjected to the inquisition in Rome and found guilty of heresy and of accepting the doctrine of Copernicus, that the earth was not the centre of the universe. He was burnt at the stake.

Galilei Galileo (1564-1642) Father of modern astronomy, built his own telescopes which were the most powerful in the world at that time. His observations supported those of Copernicus. He very carefully wrote a dialogue in which his views were under discussion without committing himself for fear of the inquisition, but nevertheless they eventually tried him and found him guilty punishing him to permanent house arrest. Lived in Tuscany with a good vineyard and contact with his daughter who was a nun living nearby. Despite his isolation he was visited by numerous philosophers and mathematicians.

The Levant Extensive fertile area along the east of the Mediterranean.

Library in Alexandria Established by Alexandria the Great in 323BC. It boasted editions of every book that had been written but was subject to many damaging events including arson and deliberate destruction by armies. Its final demise was being burned to the ground possibly in 48BC

The Royal Society The oldest scientific society in the world founded in London in 1660 to study natural knowledge. It was patronised by King Charles II, which gave it considerable strength despite its many early critics suggesting that it was spending a lot of time and money and achieving nothing of importance.

Industrial Revolution 18th & 19th centuries Came mainly from the development of the steam engine, railways and steam ships opening up the world to reasonably safe communication and ability for commerce to flourish.

Wright Brothers (Orville Wright 1871-1948 & Wilbur Wright 1867-1912) After many attempts eventually managed to coax a powered aeroplane into the air for 12 seconds in 1903.

Han Dynasty in China (206BC-220AD) Long period of stability when Chinese culture flourished and was far ahead of the West.

Sextant Instrument for measuring the angle of the sun or the pole star to the position of a ship at sea to determine its latitude. A form of sextant was invented by the Chinese during the Han Dynasty.

John Harrison (1693-1776) British Master clockmaker who won the prize for producing a robust timepiece that would enable mariners to determine the longitude. The story of this competition and those involved has been beautifully described in a book by Dava Sobel called *"Longitude"*.

James Clerk Maxwell (1831-1879) Cambridge physicist and mathematician described electromagnetic induction and the principal of the electric motor and dynamo.

Samuel Morse (1791-1872) American inventor introduced the electrical telegraph system and binary code in 1836 that could be transmitted as a message or telegram.

Alexander Bell (1847-1922) American inventor of the first successful telephone.

Guglielmo Marconi (1874-1937) Italian inventor and electrical engineer and one of the pioneers of radio transmission. Nobel Prize winner.

John Logie Baird (1888-1946) British pioneer of television, introduced broadcast television.

James Watt (1736-1819) Scottish inventor, who developed the steam engine and introduced the concept of horsepower.

George Stephenson (1781-1848) British civil and mechanical engineer who built the first inter-city railway to use steam locomotives. Renowned as the "Father of Railway".

Rudolf Diesel (1858-1913) German inventor of the diesel internal combustion engine.

Gottleib Daimler (1834-1900) German engineer and inventor of the petrol engine

Frank Whittle (1907-1996) British engineer, who invented the turbojet aero engine.

Hans von Ohain (1912-1918) German engineer and co-inventor of the jet aero engine independently but approximately at the same time as Whittle.

Christopher Columbus (1451-1506) Italian explorer, navigator and colonizer, supported by King Ferdinand of Aragon and Queen Isabella I of Castile. His four voyages across the Atlantic ocean led to European awareness of the American continent.

Vulcanisation Chemical process for converting rubber and related polymers into more durable materials.

Hendrik Baekeland (1863-1944) Belgian-born American chemist. Invented Velox photographic paper in 1893 and Bakelite in 1907. His invention of "Bakelite", an inexpensive, nonflammable, versatile, and popular plastic, marked the beginning of the modern plastics industry

Wallace Carothers (1896-1937) American chemist, inventor of nylon at DuPont.

Roy Plunkett (1910-1994) American chemist. He discovered polytetrafluoroethylene (PTFE) in 1938.

Araldite Extremely powerful glue based on a chemical reaction between a resin and a catalyst.

Stephanie Kwolek (b1926) American chemist who invented poly-paraphenylene terephthalamide, better known as Kevlar.

Andre Geim (b1958) Russian-born physicist. Professor in Manchester University. Nobel Prize (2010) for studies on graphene and Ignoble Prize for studies on levitation.

Kostya Novoselov (b1974) Russian-born physicist, Professor in Manchester University. Nobel Prize 2010 shared with Geim.

Norman Borlaug (1914-2009) American biologist. Nobel Prize for plant breeding experiments. Father of the Green Revolution

Gregor Mendel (1822-1884) plant biologist, priest and mathematician. His painstaking breeding experiments demonstrated that certain traits were genetically inherited according to mathematical principles leading to Mendel's Laws which are the basics of contemporary genetics. He was relatively unknown during his lifetime and led a quiet life as an Abbot in a monastery in Czechoslovakia.

Fritz Haber (1874-1940) German chemist, Nobel Prize in Chemistry 1918 for synthesizing ammonia for fertilizers. Fertilizers were later adapted for explosives manufacture. Haber went on to lead a team developing poison gas in the First World War. This distressed his wife to such an extent that she committed suicide.

Carl Bosch (1874-1940) German chemist and engineer. Nobel Prize 1931 in chemistry. Collaborated with Fritz Haber in producing artificial fertilizers.

Plato (427-347BC) Philosopher, mathematician, student of Socrates and teacher of Aristotle.

Alexander the Great (356–327BC) Pupil of Aristotle. Waged war with spectacular success throughout Middle East, Egypt and Pakistan. Overthrew the Persian King Darius III .

George Stubbs (1724-1806) British painter. Known for his accurate and beautiful painting of horses.

Pompeii & Herculaneum Towns near Naples which were destroyed in 79AD by the eruption of the volcano Vesuvius

Fracking Forcing fractures in rock layers, by pressurized fluid to extract oil and gas.

Aristotle (384-322BC) Polymath, philosopher, scientist and mathematician. Studied every subject to which he turned his attention especially biology, astronomy, mathematics and philosophy

Feng Shui Metaphysical practice in the orientation of buildings and layout of household goods to ensure good fortune.

Siege of Orleans (1428-1429) During the 100 years war between France and England, Joan of Arc led the French to an initial victory.

Alfred Nobel (1833-1896) Founder of the Nobel Prize, Swedish chemist, engineer, innovator, and armaments manufacturer. Inventor of dynamite.

Johannes Gutenberg (1395-1468) German blacksmith, goldsmith, printer, and publisher who introduced printing to Europe.

Karl Marx (1818-1883) German philosopher, economist, sociologist, historian, journalist, and revolutionary socialist who developed the theory of international communism and did most of his writing whilst living in London.

Nicolaus Copernicus (1473-1543) Polish mathematician and astronomer who formulated a heliocentric model of the universe which placed the Sun, rather than the Earth, at the centre.

Isaac Newton (1642-1727) Cambridge mathematician and physicist who analysed the nature of light, splitting white light into the colour spectrum and describing the force and properties of gravity and the behaviour of moving objects. Also, together with the German mathematician, Leibliz, invented the Calculus.

Johannes Keppler (1571-1630) German mathematician and astronomer who described the laws of planetary motion fundamental for Newton's theory of gravitation.

"The Origin of the Species" published on 24 November 1859, a work of scientific literature by Charles Darwin which is the foundation of evolutionary biology.

Linnean Society Founded in 1788 The world's oldest extant biological society based in London. It remains a leading modern forum for debate and discussion of natural history in all its branches

Genotype & Phenotype "Genotype" is an organism's full hereditary information. "Phenotype" is an organism's actual observed properties, such as morphology, development and behaviour. This distinction is fundamental in the study of inheritance of traits and their evolution.

Charles Babbage (1791-1871) Cambridge mathematician and inventor whose clockwork computer was based on principles that justified regarding him as the "father of computers".

Transistor semiconductor device to amplify and switch electronic signals and electrical power. Successor of the glass valve.

Alan Turing (1912-1954) English mathematician and computer pioneer who developed an electromechanical machine used to break German codes. Thus eventually evolved into a huge and effective computer known as the "Colossus" which half-filled a room and was of central importance in the successful code breaking in World War II.

Grace Hopper (1906-1992) American computer programmer who found a moth in her computer which undermined its working.

Gordon Moor (b1929) American computer scientist who foretold the extraordinarily rapid evolution of the computer accurately.

Chapter III

Steven Pinker (b1954) Canadian experimental psychologist, cognitive scientist, linguist, and popular science author.

Saddam Hussein (1937-2006) Brutal dictator of Iraq who was both wooed and then hated by the West and eventually defeated by Western Powers in the second Iraq war.

Otto von Bismarck (1815-1898) Chancellor of Germany who united the independent states and forged the German-speaking peoples into a powerful and militarised nation.

Sunni, Shia and Alawite All important religious sects united in the religion of Islam but persistently at war with each other due to disputation of the interpretation of the religion.

Mohamed Bouazizi (1984-2011) Tunisian street vendor who set himself on fire on 17 December 2010, in protest at the confiscation of his wares, harassment and humiliation. This triggered the start of the "Arab Spring".

Francis Bacon (1561-1626) English philosopher and poet who expressed important concepts of politics and culture leading to the scientific method.

Professor Stuart Firestein - Published *"Ignorance – How it drives science "* Experimental neurologist at Columbia University, New York

MMR vaccine against measles, mumps, and rubella (also called German measles). It is a mixture of live attenuated viruses of the three diseases, administered via injection. It was first developed by Maurice Hilleman while at Merck

Andrew Wakefield (b1957) British physician, known for his fraudulent 1998 research paper in support of the now-discredited claim that there is a link between the administration of the measles, mumps and rubella (MMR) vaccine, autism and bowel disease.

status epilepticus A dangerous condition of continuing seizures which eventually lead to death.

Hemiplegia Paralysis of the arm, leg, and trunk on the same side of the body, the result of damage to the opposite side of the brain.

Phineas Gage (1823–1860) American railroad construction foreman remembered for his improbable survival of a rock blasting accident in which a large iron rod was driven completely through his head, destroying much of his brain's left frontal lobe, and for that injury's reported effects on his personality and behaviour over the remaining 12 years of his life.

CHAPTER IV

Aldous Huxley (1894-1963), George Orwell (1903-1950), British novelists coming from opposite political spectra who approached the consequences of new technologies and brutal coercive dictatorship of the state.

Patrick Montgomery (1922-1995) Dermatologist at Guys Hospital, London with a remarkable talent for writing the lyrics for amateur musical medical parodies

Sword of Damocles Greek legend of a continuous threat of death at any time.

Francis Galton (1822-1911) Nephew of Charles Darwin, expounded theories of breeding which extended to humans and were hijacked by political dictators including Hitler.

Angela Merkl (1954 -) German Chancellor of Germany since 2005 and the leader of the Christian Democratic Union since 2000.

François Hollande (1954 -) President of France.

Wilhelm Röntgen (1845-1923), German physicist, who in 1895, produced and applied to medicine electromagnetic radiation known as X-rays or Röntgen rays. Nobel Prize.

Henri Becquerel (1852-1908) Nobel Prize shared with Marie Curie. Discoverer of radioactivity.

Uranium/plutonium Unstable heavy elements used in radiation applications including the development of thermonuclear weapons and atomic energy plants.

Radioisotopes elements with unstable nuclei which emit irradiation spontaneously for example α, β and γ rays.

Fred Hoyle (1915-2001) English astronomer noted primarily for his contribution to the theory of stellar nucleosynthesis and his often controversial stance on other cosmological and scientific matters.

CHAPTER V

William Harvey (1578-1657) English physician, described the circulation of the blood.

Joseph Lister (1827-1912) British surgeon who introduced the antiseptic technique to avoid surgical sepsis.

Ignaz Semmelweis (1818-1865) Austrian physicist who introduced hygienic practices in labour wards which reduced sepsis and death after childbirth.

Edward Jenner (1749-1823) English physician who introduced vaccination against smallpox.

Florence Nightingale (1820-1910) celebrated British social reformer, and founder of modern nursing. She came to prominence while serving as a nurse during the Crimean War, where she cared for wounded soldiers

Gerhard Domagk (1895-1964) German pathologist and bacteriologist, discovered Sulfonamidochrysoidine (Prontisil) the first commercially available antibiotic. Received the 1939 Nobel Prize

Alexander Fleming (1881-1955), Ernest Chain (1906-1979) , Howard Florey (1898-1968) These three biologists described and developed penicillin in England and were co-recipients of the Nobel Prize.

MRSA (*Methicillin-resistant Staphylococcus aureus*), **CD** (*Clostridium difficile*) Two bacteria notorious for their resistance to most antibiotics. Have become an increasing cause of mortality and morbidity in the past 20 years

Christopher Wren (1632-1723) English architect, mathematician and polymath. Designed St. Paul's Cathedral, London

Paul-Louis Simond (1858-1947) French physician and biologist who demonstrated the transmission of bubonic plague from rats to humans by fleas

St. Benedict (480-534) Introduced code of conduct for monks. Founder of the Benedictine Order

Peter Medawar (1915-1987) Innovative biologist and philosopher who studied the immunity of rejection and discovered immunological tolerance. Nobel Prize.

Joseph Murray (1919-2012) Plastic surgeon in Boston who performed the first identical twin kidney transplants in humans. Nobel Prize.

Mercaptopurine (6-MP or its brand name Purinethol) Immunosuppressive drug closely related Azathioprine - (AZA) drug used in organ transplantation.

Monoclonal antibodies developed by George Kohler and Cesar Milstein in Cambridge in 1975 who shared Nobel Prize.. They have a special property of targeting a single molecule in the manner predicted by Paul Ehrlich as a "magic bullet."

"Campath" Earliest monoclonal antibody, powerful immuno-suppressant and anti-cancer drug.

"prope" Latin for "almost" used in the context of powerful induction treatment followed by minimal maintenance immunosuppression in recipients of organ grafts.

DNA & RNA These nucleic acids carry vital genetic information DNA is a double stranded molecular which contains the "alphabet" of genetic instructions. RNA is a single stranded molecule which acts a transcripting messenger from DNA to protein synthesis.

Inner cell mass collection of cells in the in the very early embryo that will give rise to the definitive structures of the foetus. Separated these cells are called embryonic stem cells and each can give rise to a whole foetus.

Pluripotent embryonic stem cells can form any tissue in the foetus. Stem cells from adult tissue can behave like an embryonic stem cells They are called induced pluripotent stem cell (iPS)

Dolly the sheep - (5 July 1996 – 14 February 2003) was a female domestic sheep. The first mammal to be cloned from an adult somatic cell, using the process of nuclear transfer.

Beta cells Highly specialised cells in the pancreas located in the islets of Langerhan produce insulin.

Teratoma tumour with derivatives of more than one germ layer - may be malignant.

Shinya Yamanaka (1962 -) Nobel Prize. Japanese researcher at Kyoto University showed that adult skin cells could be dedifferentiated to a pluripotent state (iPS) similar to embryonic stem cells.

Samuel Johnson (1709-1784) English writer who made lasting contributions to English literature – produced the first English dictionary, poet, essayist, moralist, literary critic, biographer, and editor.

CHAPTER VI

Haruki Murakami (1949 -) Best-selling Japanese writer. His works of fiction and non-fiction have received critical acclaim and numerous awards, both in Japan and internationally,

Shoko Asahara (1955 -) Founder of the Japanese new religious group Aum Shinrikyo. He was convicted of masterminding the 1995 sarin gas attack on the Tokyo subway and several other crimes, for which he was sentenced to death in 2004. In June 2012, his execution was postponed due to further arrests of Aum Shinrikyo members.

Sarin Neurotoxic lethal gas, colourless and odourless. Developed in Germany in 1938.

Behring Breivik (1979 -) Perpetrator of the 2011 Norway attacks. On 22 July 2011, he bombed government buildings in Oslo, killing eight people. He then killed 69 more people, mostly teenagers, in a mass shooting at a Workers' Youth League (AUF) camp on the island of Utøya. In August 2012 he was convicted of mass murder causing a fatal explosion, and terrorism .

Charles Whitman (1941 –1966) American engineering student and former U.S. Marine, who killed sixteen people and wounded thirty-two others in a mass shooting rampage in and around the Tower of the University of Texas in Austin on August 1, 1966. Post mortem examination revealed a malignant brain tumour.

Waco Davidians religion The Waco siege was a siege of a compound belonging to the religious group Branch Davidians by American federal and Texas state law enforcement and military between February 28 and April 19, 1993.

Vernon Wayne Howell (David Koresh) (1959 –1993) was the American leader of the Branch Davidians religious sect believing himself to be its final prophet.

"Islamist" **by Ed Husain**. Book described his personal struggle in accepting terrorist doctrines and then rejecting them.

"Reluctant Fundamentalist" **by Mohsin Hamid**. Story of Changez Khan, a fictitious Pakistani intellectual who became disillusioned with Western capitalism and converted to anti-Western fundamentalism.

Marie Curie (1867-1934) Nobel Prize. Polish/French physicist described radioactivity and discovered two elements, polonium and radium utilised in irradiation treatment of cancer.

Pierre Curie (1859-1903) Nobel Prize. French physicist, collaborated with his wife Marie on the study of radioactivity.

Cathode ray tube Invented by JJ Thomson in Cambridge. He also described the electron and fundamental components of atoms.

CHAPTER VII

Martin Luther King (1929 -1968) American pastor, activist, humanitarian, and leader in the African-American Civil Rights Movement. Best known for his role in the advancement of civil rights using nonviolent civil disobedience based on his Christian beliefs. He was assassinated in Memphis.

Gregorian Calendar Also called the Western calendar and the Christian calendar, is internationally the most widely used civil calendar. The Gregorian calendar was first adopted in Italy, Poland, Portugal and Spain in 1582.

Edwin Powell Hubble (1889 – 1953) Nobel Prize. American astronomer who played a crucial role in establishing the field of extragalactic astronomy and supporting the concept of an expanding universe.

"Big Bang" Cosmological model for the birth of the Universe. The term introduced by the British astronomer, Fred Hoyle, who did not support the expanding universe theory.

Georges Lemaitre (1894 – 1966) Belgian priest, astronomer and professor of physics at the Université catholique de Louvain. He was the first to propose the theory of the expansion of the Universe.

Werner von Braun (1912–1977) German rocket engineer and the leading figure in the development of rocket technology in Germany during World War II and, subsequently, in the United States, the "Father of Rocket Science".

Sputnik 1 The first artificial Earth satellite launched in 1957. A triumph for Russian space science.

Yuri Gagarin (1934 –1968) Soviet pilot and cosmonaut. He was the first human to journey into outer space and return.

Apollo Program of the American National Aeronautics and Space Administration (NASA), was responsible for the landing of the first humans on Earth's Moon in 1969.

Neil Armstrong (1930 – 2012), American astronaut and the first person to walk on the Moon.

Gaia Greek goddess, mother of the earth.

The Milky Way The galaxy that contains our Solar System. Its name "**milky**" is derived from its appearance as a dim glowing band arching across the night sky.

Ricin Highly toxic, naturally occurring lectin (a carbohydrate-binding protein) produced in the seeds of the castor oil plant *Ricinus communis.*

Alexander Litvinenko (1962-2006) Former officer of the Russian KGB, fled from court prosecution and received political asylum in the United Kingdom.. On 1 November 2006, Litvinenko suddenly fell ill and was hospitalized. He died three weeks later, becoming the first confirmed victim of lethal polonium-210-induced acute radiation syndrome.

Polonium Chemical element with the symbol Po and atomic number 84, discovered in 1898 by Marie and Pierre Curie. A rare and highly radioactive element with no stable isotopes. Polonium is chemically similar to bismuth and tellurium, and it occurs in uranium ores.

Botulin toxin protein and neurotoxin produced by the bacterium *Clostridium botulinum.* It is the most acutely toxic substance known

Botox Drug used as an anti-ageing cosmetic, made from a toxin produced by the bacterium *Clostridium botulinum.* The same toxin that causes a life-threatening type of food poisoning called botulism.

Anthrax Acute disease caused by the bacterium *Bacillus anthracis.* Most forms of the disease are lethal, and it affects both humans and animals.

CHAPTER VIII

James Collip (1892 –1965) Canadian biochemist, member of the Toronto group which isolated insulin.

Charles Hull (1939 -) American technologist who patented 3D printing techniques based on printing from designs solid objects in thin layers of material that solidified on exposure to ultra violet light or lasers.

EMP Electromagnet pulse in a short violent energy burst that can damage electronic equipment similar to the effect of a strike of lightening.

AUTHOR CONTACT INFORMATION

Dr. Sir Roy Calne
Emeritus Professor of Surgery
Dept. of Surgery and Medicine
University of Cambridge, UK
Visiting Professor
Dept. of Medicine and Surgery
National University of Singapore
22 Barrow Road Cambridge CB2 8AS, UK
calne@hermes.cam.ac.uk

INDEX

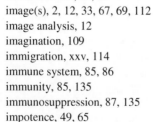

V

vaccine, 55, 76, 122, 132
valve, 44, 131
variations, 8, 44
varieties, 28
vehicles, 25
vein, 83
versatility, 109
vessels, xvii, 15, 75, 83
victims, 2, 39, 49, 96, 124
Vietnam, 39
violence, xxv, 49, 60, 66, 69, 97, 98, 117, 118
violent crime, 49
viruses, 45, 77, 78, 81, 105, 106, 132
vision, 12, 70, 78
vulnerable people, 67

W

walking, 53, 64
wall painting, 15
war, xvi, xxi, xxii, xxiii, xxv, xxvii, xxviii, 3, 4, 6, 8, 12, 13, 16, 23, 25, 26, 27, 30, 38, 39, 48, 49, 104, 105, 106, 117, 121, 124, 130, 132, 134
watches, 19, 21
water, xxiv, 13, 15, 26, 27, 30, 31, 59, 71, 72, 76, 77, 117
water resources, 31

watershed, 87
weapons, xx, xxi, xxiii, xxvi, xxvii, 2, 3, 4, 5, 7, 8, 15, 16, 19, 30, 31, 35, 36, 38, 39, 40, 45, 48, 70, 94, 95, 96, 103, 104, 105, 106, 110, 111, 112, 114, 119, 124, 134
weapons of mass destruction, 48
Western countries, 3, 49, 52, 59, 63
Western Europe, 13, 17
whistle blower, 122
white blood cells, 85
wind turbines, 28
wires, 22, 26, 64
wood, 15, 27, 37, 41
wool, 123
workplace, 45
World War I, 7, 30, 93, 103, 111, 131, 138
World Wide Web, xxi, 122

X

x-rays, 69, 70

Y

yellow fever, 81
young people, 94

Z

zinc oxide, 28